The Extreme MakeOver

The Five Areas of Prosperity

Iman,

May God Continue
to Bless and Keep You!!!
Much Success to You!

Lisa M. Jones

The Extreme MakeOver

The Five Areas of Prosperity

BY *Lisa M. Jones*

Unlock Publishing House
231 West Hampton Place
Capitol Heights, MD 20743
www.unlockpublishinghouse.com
1 (240) 619-3852

Edited by Mary Arnold

Cover design by Wallicia McCaskill

Unlock Publishing House is not responsible for any content or determination of work. All information is solely considered as the point of view of the author.

ISBN: 978-0-9855261-1-5

Acknowledgments

There are no words that can sum up my heartfelt gratitude for all of the wonderful supporters and encouragers I have been blessed to encounter.

A special thank you goes out to my Parents, Walter and Angela Patten, for always supporting me through the many endeavors upon which I have embarked. I love you more than words can express and I will never be able to fill the thirst for showing you my appreciation whether it is in my walk, talk or giving. You are the best parents one could ever ask for.

To Shanina L. Jones, my daughter, my Chef. I am so blessed to have a wonderful child like you. I love you and I am so proud to be your mom. You have brought so much joy to my life. Keep pressing my child; you are going to make a difference in this world. Thank you for your support.

To my siblings: Pam, Kevin, Bridgett, Lynn, Walter, Jr. and Tressa. You have supported me throughout the years. I love and appreciate you. A special thank you to my sister Bridgett V. Patten, who every time I make a call for help is there with no questions asked. I am forever grateful.

To my personal assistant, Andrea L. Jackson: You are my friend, my confidante, my family, my personal assistant, my business partner and my truth teller. I am a better me as a result of knowing you. I thank God for placing you in my life. You have helped me through some rough times and I am forever grateful. Thank you, Shauna and Nia (cousins) for lending your mom to me from time to time. Thank you so much for keeping me accountable to be who God has called me to be. I appreciate you.

To Leslie V. Corbin, my God what can I possibly say to express the many great times we have had over the years. You have been my friend for over 25 years. I am forever grateful for the joy you have brought to my life. I trust and love you. Thank you for always being there and for your constant support and encouragement.

To Dr. Karen Bethea, Pastor, the love I have for you is so deep in Christ that it is hard to express. You are my Correction, Direction and Protection. I love your boldness in Christ Jesus. Thank you for never wavering and never giving up on me. I am a better person today as a result of being under your covering. I admire the Christ in you and I desire the same joy and peace you have in his name. Thank you for your time and patience. You are the real deal. There is nothing fake. *Set The Captives Free Outreach Center* is a ministry that God truly uses to Set the Captive Free. I love you.

Mike Evans, My Mentor, My Friend, My brother in Christ. I do not know how to express my appreciation for you. When I was at a very low point you and your wonderful wife Regina Evans welcomed me into your home and I was healed. God used you guys at a very low time in my life. I am forever grateful. Thank you for being the Peacekeeper in my life. For overnighting me the caramel/cheese popcorn (smile). For never giving up on me. You are a great business man and I am honored to be under your tutelage.

Pastor Dawn Harvey, my publisher, my encourager, my supporter. Thank you and "Unlock Publishing" for being so patient with me. I appreciate you so much. I am loving our new found friendship and I have so much respect for you. You are a wonderful Woman of God and He is going to use you mightily. May God continue to bless you and restore one hundredfold all that you so graciously give out to others.

To my Primerica Financial Services family: I am a better leader, friend, Christian, mother, daughter and believer today because of my affiliation with you. Thank you my new found family for all the encouragement and love you have shown me over the years. It has been seventeen years of growth, accountability, fun and exposure to some of the greatest people one can ever meet. I wish that all could and would be so lucky. God Bless You.

Foreword

Man is a triune being. He is spirit, soul and body. In order to be whole or healthy one must devote adequate time to developing all three aspects of their being. It is impossible to separate the three distinct segments of who we are. Though they are separate they are intertwined in a way that makes them all necessary for health. Our spirits must be connected to their creator in order to thrive and flourish, Psalm 1:1-3. In the words of the United Negro College fund, "The mind is a terrible thing to waste." It is a muscle that must be exercised through thought, meditation, and new information. Our bodies are like a well built machine which require maintenance in the form of healthy eating, care and exercise. In this book Lisa M. Jones expounds on the five areas of prosperity. Life is not just about making money. It is about being rich in relationships, character, health, wisdom and sound financial choices. Enjoy this work that is sure to bless you!

Dr. Karen S. Bethea, Senior Pastor
Set the Captives Free Outreach Center
President, The Women Who Soar
Baltimore, Maryland

Table of Contents

Introduction

I am excited about this book, "*The Extreme MakeOver.*" I believe the readers will truly benefit from the knowledge that is shared throughout the chapters. The men and women who say I want more out of life than just existing will benefit the most. I want to make a difference. I want to help my community, my church the youth. I want to make an impact in this world in some kind of way. Who will benefit? The men and women who want to know how to do this. The five areas of prosperity is the ticket. These five are: Spiritual/Belief, Mental/Self-Esteem, Relationships, Physical and Financial.

If you work on becoming a better you, only then can you see the beauty in others. If you see the world as a negative place, chances are you are a negative person. If you have a trust issue, chances are you do not trust yourself to make wise decisions. If you cannot seem to build healthy relationships, chances are there is something missing inside of you. Growing in the five areas of prosperity can fix all of that. It allows you to work on you and then you will notice the change in the people around you.

Understand that if you do not decide to change and get better you will not be in the same place next year. You will either decrease or increase. I have heard people say nothing changed this year I am still in the same place. I say to them that is impossible. Because the world is always revolving, you cannot stay in the same place. Something either decreased or increased in your life; and it was in one of the five areas.

Either your spiritual/belief increased or decreased. Your mental strength/Self Esteem either increased or decreased. Your relationships/social status either increased or decreased. Nobody really wants to hang around a person who is always complaining about this thing called life. Your physical never stays the same. It is a constant battle to keep it in order, so did it increase or decrease? Your financial position never stays the same because the cost of living is constantly changing. What you bought with $20 last year and what you can purchase this year is totally different. *The Extreme MakeOver* will explore how to move from average and ordinary to extraordinary, how to enact change, and how to restore oneself back to a whole woman/man. By exploring the five areas of prosperity: Spiritual, Mental, Physical, Relationships, and Financial, readers will tackle the timeless question of how to be the best me I can be.

Lisa M. Jones

Chapter I: The Extreme Makeover

What an intense title, wouldn't you say? The Extreme Makeover; is it really that serious? I would have to say, yes! When I was performing research for this book I decided to look up the definition of extreme. Webster defines extreme as the "Farthest removed from ordinary and average; exceedingly great in degree." To be made over means to improve the appearance or to change the image; to restore. I got excited about the definitions because it confirmed my belief that we are living in a time when the average and ordinary and the lack of growth is not acceptable.

I have been blessed to travel the world and speak for many organizations. I am often approached by men and women who are absolutely wonderful, but cannot figure out why their lives are not prospering and why they do not feel fulfilled. They feel like something is missing and they cannot quite figure out what it is. This always grieves me because I love to see people grow and conquer their fears. I would pray, "Lord please tell me what to say to these people because I sincerely want to help them."

I have never wanted to be a speaker that just made jokes, spoke a few deep quotes and left the stage. I have also never wanted to be looked at as just a motivational speaker. I want to be seen as an inspirational speaker. Motivation is necessary but it does not cause one to change or to act. It simply makes one feel good for the moment. In order to change and to act on new found knowledge, one must be inspired.

So, because of that deep desire, I felt so much pressure on me when I did not have the answer for the many people who would stand in line to ask me a question, take a picture or request my autograph. "Lord, use me" was always my request. I could answer some of the questions but when that man or woman stood there with tears in their eyes I would always look for the root of the issue. Then one Sunday I was at a service at "Set The Captives Free

Outreach Center" as Pastor, Dr. Karen Bethea was preaching on the five areas of prosperity: Spiritual Prosperity, Mental Prosperity, Relationship/Social Prosperity, Physical Prosperity and Financial Prosperity.

My spirit man leaped for joy because finally I figured it out. It was the most powerful message I had heard at that point. It was very difficult to sit still because Pastor was talking and the Holy Spirit was ministering to me at the same time. That message brought forth so much understanding. When Pastor Karen brings forth a word she acts it out, gives great references, tells a story, cuts and sews you back up with love -- all at the same time. It is the most powerful deliverance. I have never left the service wondering or confused about the message. It is delivered with great understanding because she is not there for show but to help the people. That message happened over three years ago and it has never left my heart. Every speech that I have put together since that point has been based around those five areas of prosperity. I even perform self evaluations based on these areas. Now, when that wounded man or woman approaches me I immediately listen for the areas that are on track and the areas that are lacking. It is the best method of evaluation that I have ever used. I can answer the questions, make recommendations and lead them in the right direction. Because I understand the five areas so much, whenever I feel low or empty I know exactly what is needed. When I speak, many are healed because they now know what it takes to be a whole man or a whole woman. When I changed my message to reflect these areas the calls started coming in to speak more frequently because it takes a boldness to really talk about these areas.

The message is rather piercing and in your face. But remember the title of the series is "The Extreme Makeover." It is not going to be a passive message. It is a message of love and understanding though. Most pastors or leaders will shy away from addressing these five areas in great detail because one could potentially get offended at the accountability that is required to prosper in these areas.

Once again I give God honor for placing me under the covering of Pastor Karen Bethea because she is truly about the souls of the people and not the number of people that are on the roster. As a result of her obedience the overflow of membership is amazing Sunday after Sunday.

It is imperative that one understands that we will never really master these five areas. I believe there must be thousands of levels in each area. We just keep growing until we get better and reach another level. We start feeling better about ourselves and more secure. We start loving and trusting our judgment a little more. We start feeling like we can love others and are more compassionate towards there needs. We stop walking in offense by understanding the true reason one would do what they did. We learn to discern what the roots of the issues are in ourselves as well as in others.

I always say to people that if I know what the root of the issues are I do not get upset when one rises up against me. If I love me, it is so much easier to love others. If I respect myself, I can respect others. If I trust myself, I can trust others. If I have a positive attitude then I can find the positive in others. I do not look for the bad, although we know that there are people that have evil spirits, I am not blind to that fact, but I immediately try to find the good.

In learning about the five areas, I have learned to forgive more. Over the years I have had people to betray me in ways I never thought possible. I was so naïve as to how people who you have helped and supported could actually one day turn on you. After hearing this message and evaluating that person's life style, belief system, relationship issues I was shocked more at me for giving those individuals so much space in my mind and heart. So, as you can see the levels are many and the life lessons are more rewarding than you may think.

Whenever I speak on these five areas I can actually see the transformation take place in the audience. It is so amazing to watch this take place. I believe people are fed up with the stage talk and the smoothing over of the real issues. They want to know what is going on inside of them and how they can fix the problem. I love seeing revelation take place. The Extreme Makeover is necessary today. There is a saying: what you don't know won't hurt you;" well, my friend, I say what you don't know will kill you. We cannot afford to slip in these areas. They all compliment each other and each is equally important.

You may ask how do I start to enact this makeover process? We will start in the next chapter which is the first area of prosperity – Spiritual/Belief.

Chapter I Journal Pages

Chapter II: Spiritual Prosperity

3 John 1:2

Beloved, I pray that you may prosper in all things and be in health, just as your soul prospers.

Spiritual Prosperity is in direct correlation with your belief system. We operate under systems in life. In other words how we raise our children, majority of the time, is based on the system in which we were raised. Corporate has a system, business owners have a system. Everything is a system; whether right or wrong we have a guideline that is followed. The guidelines are not necessarily in writing, but it becomes a natural part of us based on who we follow.

James Lane Allen wrote:

"The outer conditions of a person's life will always be found to reflect their inner beliefs."

We need to have a stronger connection to our belief system or in some cases change them. It is amazing how I can know the right way to handle a situation but still desire to do the opposite. Therefore, growing in this area is key to living the lifestyle I choose to live.

Now remember we are going to discuss all five areas. All five areas are very important, but if you do not get this area fixed the other four will not really fulfill you. There is a saying, "You either believe in something or fall for anything." Once you connect to your belief system and that system is in order, nothing can sway you from your game plan, goals and aspirations.

For those who believe, no proof is necessary. For those who don't believe, no proof is possible.

~ Stuart Chase"

My Spiritual Beliefs carried me through the process:

Sixteen years ago I decided that I wanted to be an entrepreneur. Understand, this was a big step for me because prior to this decision I had been working in the corporate system for over twenty years. All of my family and friends worked for and only understood the corporate system. When I decided to take this leap of faith into a totally new area and way of life the reception was not all that warm. We often fear the unknown. My immediate family was willing to listen, but like any family that loves their sibling, daughter and friend, they were a little nervous about my decision. It was okay to entertain the idea as long as I did not let the corporate job go. It was one of the most challenging decisions I had ever made. I was going to be a successful woman in business with so many odds against me. I was a single parent, living with my parents and had no car. Not to mention that I had decided to enter into the financial services world and my credit was poor, no money in the bank and I had no idea how the banking industry or stock market worked. Not only did I know my shortcomings but so did my family and friends. I tell you I had to believe in myself extra hard because it was pretty lonely out there. I started using the only belief system I knew and that was my Spirituality.

I was a teenager when I started studying the Bible. I will never forget being the only teenager in a women's Bible study group. I was fifteen years old and the other members were old enough to be my mother. They were the best group of women I could have known at that time because I did not desire the ways of the world like my peers. I just wanted to know more about God the Father, God the Son and God the Holy Spirit. The study group got together every Thursday at 7pm at the home of one of the members. That member was responsible for bringing forth the lesson and serving the other members. I looked forward to that session every Thursday. My thirst to know the word grew from week to week. The seeds that were sown into me are the reason I am the adult I am today. My belief in God keeps me when all else seems to fail. I know that there is nothing that can happen today or any other day that God and I cannot handle. Together we are a powerful force. I am willing to follow and He is willing to lead. I am humble at the thought of Him using me as a vessel to touch others lives. I thank my parents for starting off my foundation in the Christian community and for allowing a fifteen year old girl to join a Bible study with women of great wisdom. So you can see my Spirituality kept me, protected me, humbled me and lead me throughout life.

I started quoting scriptures that supported my goals and dreams. I started speaking success over my life and doing affirmations. I had to convince the most important person that I could do it and that was me. Napoleon Hill said "One must marry one's feelings to one's belief and ideas." My circle of people began to change because I needed to be around people who would support my ideas and encourage me to move forward. I started hanging around a group of people who challenged me to do well in my new found business. It was challenging and exciting all at the same time. My belief system started to increase with not just every victory, but with every failure as well. You may say how can it increase with failure. Well I learned that failure is never final unless you quit.

I started pursuing the necessary licenses that were required to be a Personal Financial Analyst. After failing the state exam the first time I did not get discouraged because I could go back and take it again. At night I would have self talks that were positive and encouraging. I would listen to tapes and go to seminars to hear from successful men and women of all backgrounds and nationalities. Whenever I wanted to give up I just kept saying God would never set me up to fail. I would quote:

Numbers 23:19

God is not a man, that he should lie, nor a son of man, that he should change his mind. Does he speak and then not act? Does he promise and not fulfill? (NIV)

The answer to me was no. I would say, Lisa you were ordained to be and to do great things. I started believing that I was called to make a difference. I later joined a church that was strong in the word and had a piercing message for the people. The accountability to believe more and walk in expectation grew more and more. I found myself entering into levels of belief that were not familiar, but made perfect sense. I surrounded myself with other believers and although the naysayers were plentiful the believers were stronger. I started growing in my spiritual walk and the prosperity kicked in. At this point no one could cause me to question my ideas and belief. I knew that what I was doing in my business was right and people were benefiting from the knowledge that I shared. (You will hear more about that knowledge in the fifth area of prosperity).

One of my favorite books is the Bible. That is where I get all of my wisdom and encouragement.

Proverbs 1:5

"A wise man will hear and increase learning, And a man of understanding will attain wise counsel."

I started seeking counsel from successful leaders who had a qualified opinion. In other words, if you decided you were going to college but you wanted to get the opinion from family and friends, would you seek out the counsel from the ones who never went to college or who dropped out. No, you want to get a qualified opinion from the ones who stuck it out and completed the task at hand. Now I do believe in

26

learning from everyone but I look for qualified opinions when searching for direction. Every year I would evaluate my growth and I started noticing that wisdom does not hide its face from us. We either run to it or away from it. I realized that part of growing spiritually was being accountable for my actions. Therefore, I sought out a mentor who had this area of their life in order and shared the same belief system as I.

Matthew 7:7

[Ask, Seek, Knock] "Ask and it will be given to you; seek and you will find; knock and the door will be opened to you..." (NKJV)

So often I meet people who want to grow, start a business, climb the corporate ladder and it never happens. Why, because they do not ASK, SEEK or KNOCK. You have to ask for what you want. Seek wise counsel and knock on some doors to find it. Once you are accountable to someone the chances of achieving that goal is greater than leaning to your own understanding.

It was not as easy as it may sound. I questioned my abilities, I had my doubts and I was not as strong as I needed to be when I ventured out into the entrepreneurial world. The naysayers sometimes got the best of me. Once again, because I was working on prospering spiritually, I learned to allow people to be who they are and not let them dictate my decisions, beliefs, opinions or outcome. I took control over my life and my attitude. I was no longer a victim. I took ownership for my actions. When you learn the value of a qualified opinion it can truly carry you a long way. My daily prayer to God was for Him to show me who should have my ear. Show me the people who have your ear and I will show you your bank account, your neighborhood, your destiny, your family structure, your belief system, your attitude, your self esteem – it is never ending.

Ask yourself, what do I truly believe in? What is my purpose? What was I created to do while on this earth? Am I living or just existing? I believe one can only answer these questions when they have a firm belief system. Again I say, you either believe in something or you will fall for anything. I believe that something must be bigger than you. Know that your brain has taken you as far as you are right now at this moment. It is going to take something stronger, wiser and more disciplined than you to get you further. I embraced this wisdom and it is still carrying me today.

My Spiritual Prosperity is growing daily. The more it grows the more confident I am. The more it grows the stronger I am. The more it grows the more positive I am and the more it grows the more I enjoy life. I still experience life's difficulties and there are still bumps in the road but I can handle it better because of my personal intimate relationship with God the father, God the son and God the Holy Spirit. I honestly do not think I could handle this world today if I did not have my beliefs. I see so much hurt in people and I truly believe they are searching. We are not beyond reproach, it is a thin line. When I call on the name of Jesus I feel a sense of peace, then my conquering spirit kicks in and I know that I can handle all things and that I am not alone. I wish for you and for all, that same feeling could overwhelm you. I laugh in the face of adversity because I believe in the great I AM. Alone I am weak but with Him I am strong.

This area of prosperity helps me to see the other four areas more clearly. I have eyes to see and ears to hear. It causes my vision to be clearer and my thought process to be sharper. Therefore, I grow daily and I praise Him daily for understanding.

Will we ever reach the top level? I do not think so, that is why life is so much fun. Every day is a new day full of possibilities. I am smiling as I write this because I am so grateful for the possibilities. I have another chance to get it right and to go to another level. Like I stated before, it is not always pleasant. At times it feels overwhelming but I cannot imagine where I would be without my challenges, trials and tribulations. It sounds crazy but I smile as I think about all I have accomplished in the midst of a storm. A storm is sure to come and you never know in what fashion it will appear. I say to you when this happens even the nonbeliever turns to someone or something. I personally turn to my spiritual beliefs and it gets me through. I have learned to focus on the prize and not the price. When you focus on the price, it can cause you to lose your sanity. When you focus on the prize, the victory, the end results, the outcome, you get a peace that surpasses all understanding.

Lisa, how do you know this? I have experienced a lot in my years; good and bad. In all of my experiences I have learned a great lesson or two. At the end of the storm I always wind up thanking God and I realize that the situation was not as big as I thought it was. Conquering is a great feeling, but when you do not acknowledge that higher being, you do not believe it is possible. Therefore, one tends to stay in their stuff. Have you ever heard somebody tell the same story of a bad experience over and over again, or talk about an experience that happened years and years ago? Spiritual Prosperity will help you to conquer that emotion so that it will not consume you and your life. I believe at the beginning of seeking a deeper belief one must ask for forgiveness, forgive themselves and seek wisdom.

You see, I have decided not only to be happy but to walk with joy in my heart. How is this possible when things are going wrong? Well, in this book that I believe in called the Holy Bible there is a message on how to conquer every experience and at the end of this book, it states that we win. In every situation, I know that this too shall pass and that the joy of the Lord is my strength. Happiness sometimes comes only as a result of another person. Therefore it can change from day to day but JOY is everlasting because it is based on ones relationship with God. It is amazing at times because chaos is all around me yet I still smile. I still rejoice and I still praise my God. Joy makes me walk through the storm without falling backwards. When I fail, I fail forward. Always keeping my eyes looking ahead or looking up. Never looking back or down. Spiritual Prosperity is a very important piece to this puzzle called LIFE.

Now I am not beyond getting weak at times. When I feel myself getting weak I have someone in my life that holds me accountable and I make that phone call. This person reminds me daily of who I am and how much God loves me. That is why I believe in all areas of your life there must be somebody stronger than you, holding you accountable. Otherwise you are sure to lean to your own understanding and we all know that is a big risk to take.

So I challenge you to grow. I challenge you to get wiser. I challenge you to seek out a mentor that will hold you accountable and require you to get better. I believe in you and I know you can do it.

I also challenge you to work on you and your family's belief level (core value system). Write the mission statement for your life, for your family. Sometimes we correct our children when they are out of order; when the fact is, we never told them the mission statement for the family so that they will automatically know when they are off track. Let people know what it is going to look like and what your standards of excellence include. Who do you believe in and why? Then let it be known to everyone who enters your circle.

My Spiritual mirror is the Bible, I read it and it reads me. I must make the necessary adjustments to get and stay in order. When I get off track that fire inside will ignite and cause me to be so uncomfortable that the only recourse is to take heed and come back to what I know is right and pure. This is what I want for the people I love therefore I allow God to use me to speak to my family and friends. To God be the Glory for the great things he has done through me. I am forever grateful for the opportunity to seek His face and to walk the walk of righteousness.

2 Cor 3:16-18

> [16] *Therefore we do not lose heart. Though outwardly we are wasting away, yet inwardly we are being renewed day by day.*
>
> [17] *For our light and momentary troubles are achieving for us an eternal glory that far outweighs them all.*
>
> [18] *So we fix our eyes not on what is seen, but on what is unseen, since what is seen is temporary, but what is unseen is eternal. NIV*

Finally, my awesome mentor, Mike Evans, shared these five steps that helped him to increase his belief system.

1. A spiritual/food fast (abstaining from the eating of food for an established period of time);

2. Repentance and asking God for His forgiveness;

3. Utilized his two secret weapons:

   a. Prayer

   b. Praise;

4. Identified there are two types of praisers, and made a conscious decision to be the Initiator:

   a. Responder (after blessing)

   b. Initiator (before blessing); and

5. Make the Lord my best friend.

Let's grow together. God Bless You!!!!

Chapter II Journal Pages

Answer the following questions for Spiritual Prosperity.

1. On a scale of 1 to 5, how strong are you in this area?

_____

_____

_____

_____

_____

_____

2. What are some of the things you are doing to grow in this area?

_____

_____

_____

_____

_____

3. How often do you evaluate your growth in this area?

_____

_____

_____

_____

_____

4.	How strong are the people around you in this area?

_____

_____

_____

_____

_____

_____

5.	Who is your mentor in this area and how often do you talk to them?

_____

_____

_____

_____

_____

_____

6.	What is your personal mission statement?

_____

_____

_____

_____

_____

_____

_____

_____

_____

Chapter III: Mental Prosperity

(Catalyst to Change)

What is on your Mind? Today I fix my mind on whatever is true, whatever is worthy of reverence and honorable, whatever is just, whatever is pure, whatever is in alignment with my preordained destiny, whatever is lovely and lovable, whatever is kind and gracious and noble. These things will I meditate on and allow to consume my thoughts daily.

If only the above was automatic. I must speak this daily prayer into existence throughout my day. I want so much to be the most positive, excited, disciplined, Godly woman in the world. The fact is since the fall of man we tend to know all the wrong things to do and say. I had to admit to myself that my thoughts were not in alignment with my desires. I had to change my mindset.

Mental Prosperity is a powerful tool. If you can control your mind you can conquer anything. I get excited at the thought of mastering this area.

I can remember when I first started to attend leadership conferences. It was so exciting and powerful. I had an overwhelming desire to be great. I would listen to speaker after speaker with great intensity, taking notes and dreaming. I wanted to be just like each speaker. I thought, *"My God will I ever be that good?"* Can my vision really become a reality? I would immediately purchase the speakers' suggested reading material so that I could one day be great. I thought the keys to success were in these books. The first book recommended was "Think and Grow Rich." I read the book but I did not get it. It made no sense to me. I was also told to read the book of Proverbs found in the Bible. I could not catch that either. I later learned that the mindset I was operating under blocked my ability to understand. So I started praying for eyes to see and ears to hear.

I had to learn how to read with understanding. It started with the renewing of the mind. I had to put myself in the mindset of a student being instructed by great leaders. I was able to accomplish that goal by first researching the lives of the writers. What was their mindset when they wrote the book? What is the writer's background? What inspired them to write the book and what exactly do they want the reader to receive as a result of reading the book? It helped me tremendously. After awhile my mindset started changing and I started prospering mentally. I then graduated to purchasing books on tape; hearing the author read their story was best. It put me in the mindset to receive even faster. So you see it was not just about the words on the paper but what mindset you are in to receive the message. Two people can attend the same conference, listen to the same speaker and get two totally different messages. One can be positive and the other negative. It all depends on the individual mindset.

So there I was, going to be a big time business owner with a poverty mindset. I really had to work on this area with a vengeance. Business owners began to coach me. I did not always understand or agree with how they did things but it did not matter. As long as they did not require me to compromise my spiritual beliefs, or ask me to lie, cheat or steal I was fine. It is so amazing, because each time I submitted to the leadership of my mentors it worked out well. I became the best follower one could be. I learned that it was okay to follow, as long as I was following the right people. You have to be a great follower in order to become a great leader only to follow greater leaders. Most people are poor followers. I learned to respect my leaders and not speak ill of them. I learned that it was okay to fill in the gap if they were lacking in an area that I was stronger in. I did not need to receive the credit for my contribution I just needed to learn. The thirst to grow wiser and be a great example for others to follow grew more and more. I followed my leaders so closely that I could finish their sentences. I studied great people and how strong they were mentally. Their discipline and diligence was absolutely awesome. I could not quench the thirst for more wisdom.

I learned that my thoughts would eventually turn into words. That my words would eventually turn into my actions. So it was very important to think the right thoughts and speak the right words. My actions then started exemplifying the look of a leader. I started looking like a CEO, a successful business woman. I became disciplined and committed. My mentors knew that they could depend on me to show up and contribute to the bottom line growth. I began to speak and process situations differently. I did not get emotional about disappointments or temporary setbacks. I understood that high emotions will only breed low intelligence. I became stronger and stronger. The more I surrounded myself with positive go getters, the more I grew. My business eventually took form and I found myself leading people and speaking worldwide. It was absolutely amazing. I became like the people I admired – my mentors and other leaders in my business. I began to emulate them, but with my own identity, of course.

There is a commonality among strong leaders that no one can avoid. Their Mental Prosperity is a major priority. They are always students and they walk in total expectation. They expect to win, to prosper financially, to be free and to lead others. They chase the true American dream, FREEDOM. The weak tend to chase a big house or a fancy car. They chase, a new outfit or a higher position in corporate. Those who are strong chase freedom. The house and car are fruits of the chase but it is not freedom. I cannot put a value on wisdom. I cannot put a price on freedom. I do know it is not free though. You have to keep the prize in front of you, not the price. I had to get free mentally before anything else I wanted would come. I remember the revelation like it was yesterday.

I get excited just thinking about where I was and where I am now. I know that it is absolutely impossible to compete with ones mindset. I can tell you that you are beautiful everyday, if you do not believe it, it will not matter. I remember a poem written by C.W. Longenecker:

> If you think you are beaten, you are.
> If you think you dare not, you don't
> If you like to win but think you can't,
> It's almost a cinch you won't.
>
> If you think you'll lose, you're lost.
> For out in the world we find
> Success begins with a fellow's will
> It's all in the state of mind.
>
> If you think you are outclassed, you are.
> You've got to think high to rise.
> You've got to be sure of yourself before
> you can ever win the prize.
>
> Life's battles don't always go
> To the stronger or faster man.
> But sooner or later, the man who wins
> Is the man who thinks he can.

It was so important for me to keep a positive mindset in order to achieve the goals that I had set for myself. I learned to be very careful of whom I allowed to sow and plant seeds into me. I learned that if I could control my mind I could conquer anything. The mind is so powerful. When I think about the prophet, Paul from the New Testament, who spent most of his life in prison -- his mind was never in the same place as his physical body. Your mind can actually get you out of your physical location. What do you mean Lisa? Well, when I started my new venture into the entrepreneurial world, I did not operate in my present condition. I had to see myself in a totally different light. I had no car, I was a single parent, I worked a very demanding job that paid me very little, I was a student attending night college three days a week, I did not fully understand the industry that I wanted to start my business in and I was scared of the unknown. It was impossible to be successful operating in the mindset I had at that time. I was driven by my desire to change my circumstances. I wanted bigger and better.

Romans 12:2

And do not be conformed to this world, but be transformed by the renewing of your mind, that you may prove what is that good and acceptable and perfect will of God. (NKJV)

As a man thinketh so is he. I wrote ten affirmations that I would read out loud daily. I mean several times a day. I had to see myself as a successful business woman. I had to see myself as a leader of great followers and a leader of leaders. I had to visualize myself standing in front of the training room, churches, conferences, teaching about financial strategies and professional development. I visualized myself giving my acceptance speeches over and over long before I received the awards and promotions. A renewing of the mind was so necessary because I was surrounded by people who struggled financially. Negativity was in me and I had a poverty mindset. I understood that you had to work hard for what you want but I did not always like that idea. I had to replace the negative thoughts with positive thoughts and the negative habits with positive habits. I would literally draw a line down the middle of a sheet of paper and write the negative thoughts and habits on the left side, then write the positive thoughts and habits I had to have or create to replace the negative ones. It still works for me today. I always put whatever is on my mind on paper so I can see it more clearly and work on the situation at hand.

What a powerful computer we have called a brain. I am told that we only use ten percent of it. That is due to the mindset we are operating under.

Remember, I started a business with nothing but faith. I think this is mighty but continue to follow me as I explain further. I did not have what the world would consider a sound foundation to start from. So the naysayers would throw all kind of slurs at me like: "Are you rich yet?" "You're always in meetings, you made any money yet?" "You don't spend enough time with your child" "You're crazy, that business will never work."

It was painful at times but I learned to control my thoughts. My pastor preached a sermon one Sunday on the difference between understanding and agreeing. I can understand why one would be upset about an unfortunate situation that happened to them, I just do not agree with holding on to that pain and allowing it to consume your life. That wisdom made such a difference in my life. I started listening more closely to people when they spoke and I could sympathize with their pain without allowing it to take me under.

In other words, I knew at some point one needed to release that pain by forgiving the aggressor, forgive them or just make a decision to let it go. So when the family and friends did not agree with my new career goals I understood why they felt that way – I just did not agree. You see, if you have never built a business or dealt with the process of seed time and harvest it would be very difficult for you to see my vision. Therefore, the naysayers, the negativity, and the insecurity was all decreasing and the confidence and belief in me was increasing. My affirmations and vision started increasing more and more. My dreams got bigger and bigger and my desire to reach people worldwide got stronger and stronger. My mind started believing that I could accomplish anything I wanted to. The subconscious mind does not know the difference between fantasy and reality. So the more I quoted my affirmations out loud the more I started walking it out. The subconscious mind will eventually take over the conscious mind and you will operate in the person you believe you are. This is so powerful. I applied this principle in all areas of my life. It is truly a daily necessity in order to stay disciplined and focused. After repeating the process over and over it will become a habit.

The mind is a terrible thing to waste. You have to work it like the muscle it is. You have to protect it, develop it, nurture it, apply it, exercise it, and work it. If you do this it will take you places you never imagined being. You will accomplish greatness over and over again.

Now you must know that your mind has taken you as far as you are right now. If you want to go further it is so important to have a mentor in this area. One that will require you to do the things that will get you to the next level. I am often asked what was the defining moment that took you to the next level? My response is always the same: "When I had a clear concise mental picture of what I wanted and made a decision to get it." I believe the reason many do not accomplish their goals is because they cannot see what they want with their minds eye.

See, you build whatever you want in your mind first. Then you put a strategy on paper detailing how to get what you want, and then you walk it out. It is almost like being a robot. Once it is built in the mind you are on automatic pilot to walk it out. You start talking about it. Your passion starts exuding from you.

Pastor Dawn M Harvey wrote:

What do you find yourself thinking about most? Is it your job, your family or issues in your life? We have often heard it said that what you think about, you bring about. Our thought life is so very important as it pertains to every area of our lives. If we stay focused on the things that are important and envision ourselves as winners in every area, our thoughts are bound to lead us to success. For example, if you have never really sat down and thought about your faith or your health then your life will yield just that. You will not have a faith walk and your health will probably resemble little or no focus. At the same time, I am sure that the things you focus on will be in abundance in your life. If you focus on people or problems, there will be plenty of that running around in your life.

41

Take inventory of the things in your life that you spend the most time on; the positive and negative things. You will see the results of your thought life and it will be evident to you what you need to embrace more of in your life and what you need to run from as fast as you can. There is no escaping your thoughts. That is why it is so important for them to be healthy and positive thoughts. Your mind is always in motion. Even at night when you are asleep, there is still something going on. We dream at night. Some people even sleep walk. I know it sounds funny but if your mind has some activity when you are in a deep sleep just imagine what it is doing when you are wide awake. It is all over the place; trying to make ends meet and meet deadlines. We want to feed our minds with the things that it needs. Positive thoughts give you energy. Negative and sad thoughts can lead to depression. That is why it is very important for us to control and maintain a positive thought life.

You can do this in several different ways. My favorite way to maintain a positive thought life, or my vehicle of choice, is prayer. It guides me and grounds me. It helps me to put things in perspective. You may like to take long walks or exercise. Whatever works for you but choose something that will help you slow down just enough to focus. You need clarity. It is imperative that we see clearly when we are making decisions, big or small.

Think of your thought life as a pair of binoculars. There is a lens for both eyes and you have to look through them at the same time. The problem is one can be clear and you have to turn the lens on the other a little bit to make it as clear as the other. That is your thought life. You can see clearly in some areas but in order to make the right decision, especially for long term decisions you need to see the big picture from afar and with clarity. Binoculars give you a chance to see down the road. They allow you to see a lot further than your current location.

What you think about, your dreams and your goals allow you to see what is in store for you.

Everything has to begin somewhere. The only way to know where you are going is by truly knowing where you are. You can change your location with your thought life. You can put things into perspective and allow what you thought were failures to teach you how to go to the next level. Failures are just lessons used to take you to the next level. They are what you make them or shall we say what your thought life perceives them to be. You have to have a starting address to put your destination in your GPS. Even if you do not know the address where you are, the GPS will calculate your exact location to get you to the address you have selected as your destination. It has to know where to start. Why? Because it is necessary to have a beginning. The great thing about that is that it does not matter where you begin. The only thing that matters is where you end up. Just make the decision to start somewhere.

So where are you now? Your location is your thought life. You cannot go anywhere and stay there with any longevity if your thought life is not right. That is why so many people start so many things and never finish them. We lose focus which in turn hinders our thought life and causes the result of failure in that task or area. I am challenging you to evaluate your thought life. List the things that you spend the most time on and sort through them to determine what is really important and what is really hindering you. You can do it. You can start over anytime you want. Retrain your thoughts and watch your life transform!

Dawn M. Harvey

Change is not always comfortable, but when required it is necessary. The great thing is that the mind is so powerful. As human beings we have not even begun to utilize its power. One way to start to change your mind is to speak affirmations and change your mindset. Next, see the glass as being half full not half empty. Decide to be positive and show love. Understand how powerful the mind is; that is why everything starts there. If it is on your mind it can enter the heart, then from there it comes out of your mouth. That is why the word says sin is premeditated. You thought about it then you acted on that thought. Also, do things that will help to change your mindset, like listen to CDs and inspirational music. Listen to great speakers and read positive victory books about how people made it through.

I really want you to get this area of prosperity so let me take you to the infallible word of God. Gen 11:1-9, The Tower of Babel. Now at this time the whole earth had one language. These guys had nothing else to do but to try and build their own city and within that city they wanted a tower so tall that the top of it would reach the heavens. Look how powerful the mind is because they were working it out. They actually set out to accomplish that task and they were in agreement. See what can happen when two or more touch and agree. John Maxwell calls this the law of the Big Mo. They had momentum because they were in agreement. Now I need everybody to say "But God," yes but God saw the work of man and in Gen 11:6 *"And the LORD said, 'Indeed the people are one and they all have one language, and this is what they begin to do; now nothing that they propose to do will be withheld from them.'"*

Absolutely nothing you propose to do will be withheld from you. The Mind is a powerful tool. Change your mind, change your whole life. I wish for you nothing but the best, and most importantly, I want you to believe you deserve the best. Praise God for the powerful mind and the opportunity to change it.

In Bible Study our guide is "Walking in Victory" by Norman Robertson. In chapter eight it talks about the characteristics of a sound mind. It states the following:

A sound mind is teachable. You are open to receive wise counsel from the scripture, mentors and leadership that is lined up with His purpose for your life. You cannot get anywhere with your preconceived ideas and notions. If you know everything then why am I your leader or mentor. As much as I have grown I know that I do not sit at the right hand of God. So I humble myself to leadership.

A sound mind is controlled. Thoughts are the seed of action. 1 Peter 1:13, *"Therefore gird up the loins of your mind, be sober and rest your hope fully upon the grace that is to be brought to you at the revelation of Jesus Christ."*

A sound mind is full of God's word. Matthew 4:4, *"Man shall not live by bread alone, but by every word that proceeds from the mouth of God."* We need to meditate on and memorize Scripture verses. Pray Scriptures.

A sound mind is clean. It is washed and purified by the Word of God. It is free from impure, unclean and corrupt thoughts.

So my friend, as you can see, this requires a daily renewing of the mind. Forgive yourself, forgive others and move forward. You deserve a wonderful life of laughter and prosperity. Believe it and you shall receive it. God Bless you and remember the little train that could. I think I can, I think I can, I know I can and I will.

Chapter III Journal Pages

Answer the following questions for Mental Prosperity.

1.   On a scale of 1 to 5, how strong are you in this area?

_____

_____

_____

_____

_____

_____

2.   What are some of the things you are doing to grow in this area?

_____

_____

_____

_____

_____

_____

3.   How often do you evaluate your growth in this area?

_____

_____

_____

_____

_____

_____

4.   How strong are the people around you in this area?

_____

_____

_____

_____

_____

_____

5.   Who is your mentor in this area and how often do you talk to them?

_____

_____

_____

_____

_____

_____

6.   What is your personal mission statement?

_____

_____

_____

_____

_____

_____

_____

_____

_____

Chapter IV:
Relationship Prosperity

When people show you who they are, believe them.

~ Maya Angelou

Happiness keeps you sweet, trials keep you strong, sorrows keep you human, failures keep you humble, success keeps you glowing but only friends ... keep you going. Amen.

Dr. Mike Murdock said you have to pinpoint problem-people. The worth of any friendship can be measured by its contribution to your victories. People are different. Choose friends who make deposits into your life instead of withdrawals. Your warfare will reveal the true character of those around you.

Romans 16:17-18 states

"Now I beseech you, brethren, mark them which cause divisions and offences contrary to the doctrine which ye have learned; and avoid them. For they that are such service not our Lord Jesus Christ"

Show me your inner circle and I will show you your destiny. Show me who has your ear and I will show you your bank account. It is very important to entertain healthy relationships. All so often I find people who are striving for better, hanging around toxic people. Now I do not believe in looking down on any man except to pick him up, but I refuse to hang around a bunch of people who are not striving to get better in life. I often say, "If you love me, you will require me to get better." This goes against what I heard as a child. I often heard it this way: if you love me you will accept me the way I am.

Well, to me that sounds absolutely ridiculous. What if I am doing everything wrong and out of order? I absolutely love hanging around people who have their hands reaching up for something. They appreciate all that God has blessed them with, but know that there is so much more that He requires of them. Therefore, I surround myself with men and women of greatness. One of the contributing writers to this book is Mike Evans. Now, Mike Evans is a successful business man with Primerica Financial Services; his office is in Chicago, Illinois. Mike is not only my mentor but he is a friend. I do not get the positions mixed up because his first role in my life is mentor. I allow him to know me as a person because I believe he will advise me properly and steer me in the right direction to be the successful business woman I desire to be. He has my ear. He also has a qualified opinion because the leadership he provides for me is all based on what he has already accomplished. I do not want to be Mike but to imitate the successful traits that Mike has. What some tend to do is associate themselves with toxic people and share their dreams and aspirations with those folks, then get offended when they are not in agreement or shoot their ideas down. If I am out of order with the ideas or the game plan that I share with Mike, I trust him to tell me the truth so that I can get back on track. I am very comfortable sharing my business goals with Mike because I know that he will touch and agree with me, he will be happy for me and he will encourage me.

Matthew 18:19

Again, I tell you that if two of you on earth agree about anything you ask for, it will be done for you by my Father in heaven. (NIV)

This scripture makes so much sense to me. So if I want something out of life then it is very important that I align myself with someone who will believe in me, agree with me and walk in expectation with me. It is important that I share with those people what I want daily so that they can hold me accountable to act like a person who really wants to accomplish that which I proclaim to want. So, as you can see, relationship prosperity is very important in order to feel whole. Basically, what I am talking about is who you associate yourself with. Associations are powerful. If you want to be an eagle, you cannot hang with chickens. You must be careful about who you are connected to. I have seen many marriages end because of lack of knowledge in this area. I can remember years ago, listening to a series where Bishop T.D. Jakes talked about issues in some marriages. You have a half of a man who may be wounded from his past and never got delivered or healed and a half of a woman who is wounded from her past, trying to have a whole marriage.

I have often said to people that a man cannot fill my cup. He can only cause it to overflow. I must be secure in who I am as a woman. I must know my identity and not lose it in this world or in him. Only then can I appreciate what he has to offer to cause my cup to overflow. Only then can I accept his role in my life and treat him accordingly. There are many types of relationships and you need to evaluate all of them in order to identify their position in your life. Once you do this you put people in their perspective boxes. For example my parents are very important to me and they give me so much wisdom and love. I thank God for them daily, but they are not my business mentors *per se* because they never built a business before.

Now it does not mean that they cannot advise me on some aspects of building relationships with others or help me make decisions about a particular situation. They just do not hold the key role in my life as a business builder. What they do for me is hold me accountable to stay in touch with the mentors I have who guide my business decisions. So you must understand the role held by the people you love. What does all of this have to do with relationship prosperity? A lot; because you have to associate yourself, attach yourself, connect to, listen to or get mentored by the right people or person. Are they positive, uplifting and encouraging you to do the right things? Who has your ear? This area is so important because you can know the right things to do but because the company you keep is not in alignment with your mission statement you will find yourself going astray. Many times we hear of youth who were in the company of the wrong people and suffered the consequences of the decisions of those wrong people. Who are you hanging around? Are they positive, striving for greatness, having clean fun, serving the same God, respectful and deserving of your precious time and friendship. It is so important to spend time with the right people.

When I was at the beginning of building my business I had to learn how to mentally disconnect from people. They could be talking but it did not register in my mind because it held no value. I would mentally put up a "NO VACANCIES" sign on my forehead so that I would not rent any space to those individuals. Why, because I am more effective when I am happy, positive and encouraged. Negative people do not like any kind of company, they want negative company. I knew if I entertained the conversation it would cause me to think and act like that person. You can only control your attitude and your activity. So that was the way I stayed in control.

I meet some wonderful people in my travels and there are times they are worn out from the burdens of others. They rent space in their heart and in their mind to people who will bring nothing but grief to them. The burden from others will cause you to worry, which brings on stress, which brings on chest pains which can bring on an illness. It is simply not worth it.

There are all types of people around you, whether they are at the work place, in your church, in your household or in your family. You have "Very Needy People." These people always want for something. They cannot do anything on their own, have no fear to ask for help, and will make you believe that if you do not help them they will not make it. They cry the blues all the time.

Then there are the "Very Draining People." Oh, my goodness after talking to these people you feel like you just left a boxing match with Muhammad Ali. You are worn out.

You were happy prior to the call but now your spirits are low and you are depressed. Draining people suck all the energy right out of you.

Then there are "Very Important People." These are the people in your inner circle that you want to win for. My parents and daughter are part of my inner circle. It is not a place easily surrendered for others to enter. The people that hold that rank with me, support, encourage and hold me accountable. There are others that I did not mention that are in that circle. It is not just biological family that have reached that point with me. I treat those individuals extra special because I am a better me as a result of these people. They make deposits into my life not just withdrawals. I heard a great speaker say, "If you cannot change the people around you, then change the people around you." Where do you find these wonderful people? I found out that once I fixed me, they appeared before my eyes. I believe that when the student is ready, then the teacher will appear. My pastor, friends, business owners, business partners, siblings, and family. They were all around me. I had to open up my eyes. I had to get better.

Testimony

In remembering the old cliché "Birds of a feather, flock together," it is crazy how for years my growth was stagnant because I was flocking with chickens instead of soaring with eagles. A chicken is a bird that is not capable of sustained flight. According to http://www.birding.com, there are over 10,000 species of birds, but there were only seven listed that either could not fly or could not sustain flight. Therefore, one can conclude that flying is as natural for birds, as breathing is for humans. I am reminded of a story about a chicken and an eagle:

One day, a naturalist who was passing by a chicken farm was struck with curiosity. He noticed an eagle, the king of all birds, living among the chickens. He asked the farmer, "Why do you have this eagle confined to live in the barnyard with the chickens?"

"Since I have given it chicken feed and trained it to be a chicken, it has never learned to fly," replied the farmer. "It behaves as chickens behave, so it is no longer an eagle."

"Still," insisted the naturalist, "it has the heart of an eagle and can surely be taught to fly."

After talking it over, the two men agreed to find out whether this was possible. Gently, the naturalist took the eagle in his arms and said, "You belong to the sky and not the earth. Stretch forth your wings and fly."

The eagle, however, was confused; he did not know who he was. He was comfortable with his life and was content with the farmer providing his food and being in the company of the chickens. Seeing the chickens eating their food, he jumped down to be with them again.

Undismayed, the naturalist took the eagle on the following day up on the roof of the house and urged him again, saying, "You are an eagle. Stretch forth your wings and fly." But the eagle was afraid of his unknown self. He was afraid of the world he did not know. He was scared to fly. He jumped down once more for the chicken food.

On the next day, the naturalist rose early and took the eagle out of the barnyard to a high mountain. There he held the king of birds high above him and encouraged him again, saying, "You are an eagle. You belong to the sky as well as to the earth. Stretch forth your wings now and fly."

The eagle looked back toward the barnyard. Then he looked up to the sky. He still did not fly.

Then the naturalist lifted him straight toward the sun. The eagle looked up to the sky and began to tremble. Slowly he began to stretch his wings. He looked back once more to the barnyard and then fixed his gaze toward the sky. At last . . . with a triumphant cry he soared into the heavens.

From that moment on, the eagle was living life as an eagle. Now it may be that the eagle still remembers the chickens with a certain fondness and nostalgia. It may even be that he occasionally revisits the barnyard. But as far as anyone knows, he has never returned to the barnyard to live the life of a chicken. He truly was an eagle, even though he had lived the life of a chicken.

I spent many years of my life being with chickens and therefore I behaved as such. My social circle consisted of those who were spiritually, mentally, socially, physically, and financially in the same position as I. We were all merely existing, but not really living. Proverbs 27:17 states as iron sharpens iron, so one man sharpens another, but what if the iron is not sharp and instead the iron is dull? What I realized is much like that eagle, as I began to change and discover who I really was; if I could not change the people around me, then I had to change the people around me. Understand clearly, I do not look down on them, I love them dearly; and just like that eagle, I remember them with fondness and nostalgia, but to soar like an eagle, I had to be around eagles.

I was introduced to an environment and a circle of people who made me want to stretch. In comparison, my spiritual, mental, social, physical and financial positions looked inconsequential, at best. This group and my mentor in this group, made me want to be a better me. I always knew there was something a little different in me, but I did not know how to unlock that door of potential, that door of impact, that door of associations. My mentor gave me the key to unlock that door. As a result of unlocking that door, I am guilty by association. Guilty of surrounding myself with eagles, therefore, I began to soar.

Andrea L. Jackson

I have had the privilege of mentoring Andrea Jackson and it has been a great experience for me. The person that shared the above testimony is not the person I met ten years ago.

When I truly started to understand what a mentor was it brought about so much clarity. I always respected my elders. I understood how to adhere to authority. I honored my parents and was very appreciative of them. But I did not know what it meant to be truly mentored. I learned that a mentor is one that is more experienced or more knowledgeable, gives wise counsel and helps to guide your development. A mentor cares about developing the whole person. It is an Extreme Makeover.

This relationship requires much communication and accountability. If that mentor does not know you they cannot lead or guide you. Communication is a very important, nonnegotiable piece to this process. There must be trust and understanding. The mentor is not there to necessarily make you comfortable; they are supposed to be the truth person in your life. That is not a comfortable position to hold because often it requires the mentor to correct the mentee in areas they have never before been called on. I am honored to hold such a role in so many lives and at the same time it can be overwhelming. When you have a heart for the people, you cannot fill the thirst of helping your fellow man succeed. I have been told by many that I am mentoring them from afar. I honestly do not believe that is possible. I believe I am inspiring them not mentoring them. I cannot express enough how important it is to talk to your mentors daily. In all five areas of prosperity you should be able to write a name of a person that is mentoring you in that area. If you have one person who is able to mentor you in all five areas, you are a blessed individual. That person must walk with great wisdom. As a mentor, it is my greatest desire to be the example people need to see. I realize that my behaviors must be in alignment with what I profess. I must be congruent in all that I do and say.

Then there is the mentee. Wow what a powerful position to hold. The mindset of this person is so important. If you are not ready to receive, willing to be humble and coachable this process will not work for you. I was so surprised how at times I would shut down when I did not like what the mentor would say. Now, because the Word of God was in me, the correction kicked in right away. I was never a person to blame everyone else for my position in life. I took full ownership for who I was, the mistakes I made and what I needed to do to correct my life. I was never a victim. I would always say "Lisa, to thy own self be true."

I learned how to be a great follower. I made sure I was wherever my leaders were and I was so coachable. I remember my accountability sessions with my mentor. I went through so many emotions at that session. I would laugh, cry, rebel, be humbled, and then leave grateful. I wanted to be so good at my craft that I always gave in to the correction, protection and direction. I am often asked how can one find a mentor? My response is always when you are ready to be a mentee, you will notice all the great mentors around you. There have been folks that asked me to mentor them that really wanted a friend, someone to listen to them complain or someone to agree with their bad decisions. That is not our role in your life. We are not a dumping ground. It is so important for a mentor to stay free of negativity and victim mentality. When there is too much clutter in the mind one cannot hear clearly from God. Pray for your mentors, uphold them and appreciate them because they hold the tools and the message that you need to get to new levels. What a powerful relationship.

Now, let's not forget the other relationships in our lives, like our parents, siblings, friends, co-workers etc etc etc. I say to you that they are important too. We need to understand their roles in our lives and put them in their box. If toxic, dismiss it right away. Show them love and kindness but do not allow them to rent space in your mind. Love them, respect them as children of God but do not allow them to stop you from fulfilling your ordained destiny and precious dreams. It is so important to prosper in this area because we live in a time where your credibility and who you know can take you far. Be a person of integrity and of great character. I believe in order to be blessed you must first be a blessing. Touch people's lives in a positive and effective manner.

Testimony

> *Philippians 3:15-16*
>
> *15 All of us, then, who are mature should take such a view of things. And if on some point you think differently, that too God will make clear to you.*
>
> *16 Only let us live up to what we have already attained. (NIV)*

As I write this, my husband and I are preparing to celebrate our 25th wedding anniversary. It seems like just yesterday we were planning our wedding, getting the news about having our first child, and buying our first home. I even remember that Friday night party in my college dorm. The only party that is worth remembering because that was the night I met my future husband.

Often, people fall in love with the idea of marriage, but not the commitment. When I think about spending so much of my life with someone who was once a stranger, two questions immediately come to mind: 1) with the divorce rate in the U.S. well above 50%, why did we stay together?; and 2) what helped us to go the distance and build a life together? After 25 years, I could say it is because we are still in love with each other or I could say he is one of the sweetest people I know. He is definitely the most handsome man I know, a wonderful dad, and a very caring husband. I could say all of these things because they are all true, but as I reflect on these 25 years, it is my belief that to build a strong marriage relationship, you must have a strong foundation.

This strong foundation must be built on a solid rock that is able to withstand the storms of life, the storms that will surely come. The key to building this strong foundation is commitment. You must be willing to make and keep that commitment. Commitment is key in everything, but especially in a marriage. It can settle an area and speak volumes, even in the absence of one spouse. Wordnet Web defines commitment as the act of binding yourself (intellectually or emotionally) to a course of action. Listed below are a few reasons why commitment must take place in order to have a successful marriage or rejuvenate your current marriage relationship:

- COMMITTMENT DEFINES PREDICTABILITY: Predictability produces the security that is needed in any relationship. There is always security in knowing that your spouse will provide for you and your family. Example: When he gets paid weekly, he brings his check home to take care of the family's financial obligations

- COMMITTMENT DEFINES HOW ONE SHOULD PLAN: When you are committed to someone, all of your future plans are filtered through that commitment with that someone. A simple act of consideration when other interests arise – whether it is hanging out with buddies, other hobbies, or other friendships – could help avoid a toxic situation. Because you are committed to your mate, there has to be a consciousness surrounding that commitment. One must know and understand that decisions made do not just affect them; they affect the spouse as well.

EXAMPLE: My husband and I eat lunch together on Friday; I consciously do not plan anything during that time. If I were to ever consider changing that, it would never be without talking to him first and getting his approval.

- COMMITTMENT DEFINES YOUR PEACE: In any relationship there are phases, the first phase is ecstasy: "Where have you been all of my life?" The second phase is reality: "Why are you in my life?" During this phase human imperfections will surface, and sometimes offenses will take place. This is not an "if" statement, but in fact a "when" statement. When feelings get hurt or offenses take place, because of that commitment to your spouse and your relationship, you must look for solutions and never explore the option to leave. Even with the best intentions, as we make that commitment to go the distance in faith, there is an adversary that is waiting to kill, steal and destroy the marriage relationship. When this enemy comes against you, in the form of offense, temptation, anger, lack of communication, and many more; you must say, this is just a rocky moment in our relationship. Identify what is working against the marriage. Then, implement a solution. Keeping the commitment, as well as building a strong lasting relationship will require work and a whole lot of focus, but it is worth every minute.

Job 36:10 says that if we obey and trust God we will spend our days in prosperity and our years in pleasure. If this is true, and I believe that all things work together for my good and God's glory, when trouble comes; if it can't trace God's hand, I must truly trust his word.

Joyclen Prevost

NSD, Primerica Financial Services
New Orleans, Louisiana

My mentor, Mike Evans, and his wife, Regina, have been married for over 20 years. He offers this advice in regards to building stronger relationships. First and foremost communication is everything. Then, he suggests these five steps:

1.   Be Honest ;

2.   Keep Current;

3.   Act, Do not React;

4.   Attack the problem not the person; and

5.   Listen Intently.

Right relationships are precious. Respect them, nurture them, hold on to them and thank God for them daily. Without them I would not be what I am today. I am forever grateful to my family, friends and mentors that have held me up at times when I felt so weak. Who have expected the best from me and never allowed me to settle for the least and who hold me accountable to be a woman of my word. God Bless you and may God restore one hundredfold back to you what you so graciously gave to me and others.

Chapter IV Journal Pages

Answer the following questions for Relationship Prosperity.

1. On a scale of 1 to 5, how strong are you in this area?

_____

_____

_____

_____

_____

_____

2. What are some of the things you are doing to grow in this area?

_____

_____

_____

_____

_____

_____

3. How often do you evaluate your growth in this area?

_____

_____

_____

_____

_____

_____

4.   How strong are the people around you in this area?

_____

_____

_____

_____

_____

_____

5.   Who is your mentor in this area and how often do you talk to them?

_____

_____

_____

_____

_____

6.   What is your personal mission statement?

_____

_____

_____

_____

_____

_____

_____

_____

Chapter V: Physical Prosperity

Our bodies are like well built machines which require maintenance in the form of healthy eating, care, and exercise.

~ Pastor Karen Bethea

Oh boy, who wants to talk about this area? Well believe it or not this area plays a huge part in why some of the other areas suffer. At one point I was not attending church like I should because I had no energy to get up in the mornings. I would be mentally and physically drained after traveling and speaking all week. After I committed to a daily workout routine, getting up in the morning was not so difficult. I have so much energy now. During 2011, I learned more than ever before about the importance of prospering physically.

Unfortunately, there are times when we compromise our health to gain success and wealth, and then we spend our wealth to get our health back. This is a daily struggle for so many. When one can control their eating habits they have truly conquered something. There are so many suggestions out there as to what one should do to stay healthy so that their physical body can last more than a lifetime. I will not pretend to have this area in total control. I find myself constantly making the necessary corrections in order to achieve my desired weight goal. This I do know: exercise is essential. Eating right is nonnegotiable, and getting the proper rest is important.

I started working out after seeing a friend hooked up to all kinds of tubes in the hospital. The site of that person who was once so healthy and so strong, but now lay weak and helpless brought about a true conviction and taught me a few lessons. I believe that God wants to use me to speak to people in the masses. That is my ordained role while on this earth. I also know that I have a say in whether that manifestation takes place or not. Therefore, if I do not do my part then God cannot do His. I must be in position to receive the message and the order. I cannot be overweight, sluggish and sick. I need to be able to go and climb the steps, if necessary, in order to get the message to the people. This is why I work out daily and strive to be physically fit. It is not an easy task and I still have a distance to go to hit my target weight, but admitting my part in the plan has helped me to stay accountable in this area.

Testimony

One of the seven deadly sins is gluttony. Gluttony is habitual eating to excess. At age 27, I was a healthy size 14, 5' 9", 175 lbs., but just 10 years later I would top the scales at over 270 lbs., 5' 9", and a size 22. I looked like a backwards before and after commercial. The question: How do you gain 100 lbs and 4 sizes? The answer: Gluttony. Aristotle wrote "We are what we repeatedly do." Excellence then is not an act, but a habit. In a ten year period I had developed an almost fatal habit. This habit endangered my health and negatively affected my endurance, self-esteem and relationships. I ate for different reasons, some emotional and some physical, but at the end of the day I ate to fill a hole that could not be filled with food.

At the peak of my gluttonous period, I was literally addicted to fast foods. I ate out at fast food places morning, noon and night. I remember feeling hopeless when my clothes became too small to wear, when the seats in coach became too tight around my hips, when aisles suddenly became too narrow, when I would get winded from walking up a flight of stairs, when conversations about my weight went from humorous to cruel. But I also remember the day when I decided to make a change and the hope returned. I decided to do a 21 day Daniel fast. This fast consists of 21 days of eating only fruits and vegetables. This fast changed my life because I developed a new habit. A habit that did not end in death, but ended in Excellence.

During the fast I prayed that God would remove the taste of fast food and He did. It takes 21 days to create a habit and I had indeed created a habit – a very good habit. Not only had the Daniel fast destroyed ten years of dangerous living, but it completely changed my life. It has been six months since my fast ended and I have lost 39 lbs and 2 dress sizes. I walk/run 2 miles 5 to 6 times a week. I do not get winded when I walk a flight of stairs and I feel good about the way I look.

I refuse to get caught in the vicious trap in which I chase wealth and lose my health, then use my wealth to try to gain my health. Instead I choose life and physical prosperity.

Andrea L. Jackson

Daniel 10:3

> *I ate no pleasant food, no meat or wine came into my mouth, nor did I anoint myself at all, till three whole weeks were fulfilled.*

January 2nd of every year I set aside 21 days to do a spiritual fast called the Daniel Fast. It is my way of giving God the first part of my year. I normally ask other believers to join me. The purpose is to develop a more intimate relationship with Christ and to grow spiritually. I always ask God what would He have me to do this year to glorify the kingdom. I never wanted it to be the same, year after year.

The group of believers meet and share a few things they are praying for so that we can touch and agree through prayer throughout our day. One of the side benefits of this fast is the improvement of one's health.

The Daniel Fast
For the Body, Soul and Spirit

The Bible teaches us that we are a spirit, we have a soul and we live in a body. The Daniel Fast affects all three parts of us as we enter into a period of time for focused prayer and fasting.

The Body - Certainly our bodies are affected as our diet is changed, for some in very dramatic ways, during the Daniel Fast. Many men and women experience detoxing from caffeine, chemicals and sugar. The symptoms are most often headaches, leg cramps, fatigue and malaise (depression).

Most people lose weight during the Daniel Fast; and many report healings from diabetes, allergies, arthritis and cancer.

The Soul - Frequently referred to as "the flesh" in the Bible, the soul is also greatly impacted during the Daniel Fast. The soul is the seat of our emotions, intellect, personality and will. It is in the "soulish realm" where we experience cravings, frustration, anger . . . and even happiness.

During the Daniel Fast your soul may very well rebel against the dramatic change in your diet. Experiencing and winning this battle over the flesh is often one of the most powerful lessons of the Daniel Fast.

The Spirit - Our spirit is that born-again part of us that surrenders to God and then abides with the Father and the Son. Our spirit is filled with the Holy Spirit when we yield to Him. During the Daniel Fast, we want to put our spirit in charge of the other two parts of us. When our flesh is acting out with a craving, we take control of it with our spirit (just as a parent takes control of a rebellious child).

Fasting is always coupled with a spiritual goal. So during this time of fasting, you will want to focus on prayer, study and meditation.

An Important Question to Ask Yourself

During your Daniel Fast you will have many times when you might want to "stretch the rules" a little bit. For example, even though the guidelines say we are to drink only water . . . you conclude that herbal teas are vegetables and water is water and therefore you will go ahead and drink herbal teas during the Daniel Fast. However, I encourage you to learn a powerful spiritual lesson by asking yourself (examining your heart) the question, "Why do you want the herbal teas?"

My guess is that the answer will be, "Well I just want them. I cannot drink only water. I have to have something else."

The Daniel Fast teaches us to deny our "selves" and instead put our spirit in control over our flesh. As you plan your meals and eat your food, keep in mind that the definition of a fast is to deny food for a spiritual purpose.

What if you have health issues?

Fasting should never bring harm to the body. If you have concerns, be sure to consult your health professional before going on the Daniel Fast or making any major dietary change.

The Daniel Fast is a very healthy way to eat! So health professionals will support this eating plan, but might suggest a few modifications if you have health issues that need special attention. For example, pregnant and nursing mothers might get instructions to add fish, chicken and cheese into the Daniel Fast, but otherwise stay the course. Diabetics may need to add more carbohydrates or include chicken and fish. Also, those who are especially active either through sports, bodybuilding or vocation may need to slightly alter the eating plan.

I encourage you to check with your doctor ... and by the way, being addicted to Snickers and Coke do not count as a special need! lol

Susan Gregory

www.daniel-fast.com

The sense of accomplishment I feel every year from this spiritual fast is priceless. In doing this not only am I lifted higher but I have direction for my year. I prove to myself that I can conquer the flesh. Like listed above it is the flesh that craves the unhealthy foods which ultimately is causing so much illness in our world today.

Testimony

When we hear the words physically fit, we often think of the perfect person. Rarely do we think of ourselves as that perfect person. We envision that person as pleasing in appearance, so fine, smooth clear skin, firm muscles, flat stomach, and a six pack or as some might say, built like a brick house. In the 70's the Commodores actually wrote a song about that perfect person, "She knows she got everything a woman needs to get a man, how can she lose with what she use 36-24-36, what a winning hand! She's a brick house mighty might just lettin' it all hang out."

Okay stay with me, focus now. Like many, I struggled with this physically fit image every day. Wanting to be a size 10, in the gym every day, and eating nothing but fruit. In addition, a personal struggle with hereditary neck and facial moles (medical term for a mole is a NEVUS), added to my low self-image. I was losing the battle in the most important place, my mind. While at the gym one day, I began thinking, "Forget this, I'm tired, I'm doing too much, I'm not seeing the desired results, what are my options for fat reduction surgery." I went on and on with the stinking thinking. At the same time, my *iPod* started playing Never Give Up by Yolanda Adams. The tears began to roll and it was like WOW. I finally figured it out. Physically fit begins in the mind, then the body and the soul follow suit. You must have all three.

The dictionary defines physically fit as a state of health, well-being and the ability to perform specific aspects of sports or occupations. My definition is good health, luminous self-esteem, a positive attitude; an educated mind, determination, spiritual balance, happiness, exercise and an overall inventory check of one's self. The benefits of being physically fit, such as better health, lower risk of heart disease, frequent smiling, promotions, forgiveness, happiness and overall beauty will multiply. The wrong thoughts, like: "I can wear anything to work because nobody cares," became obsolete because I cared and I was doing this for me.

You never know, this may be the day that you run into your next supervisor, mentor, husband, wife, interviewer or get those five minutes of television fame. My new philosophy became, "Always look and feel your very best, and do this for you." Oh, and as for the moles, I educated myself on them and met with a dermatologist. I am happy to report that because I am happy being me and physically fit, the obsession with my cosmetic appearance is no longer an issue. As a bonus to my workout and physically fit life style I pray this prayer every morning.

> I am blessed with creativity, courage, talent and abundance. I am blessed with a great family, good friends, good health, faith, favor, and fulfillment. I am blessed with success, supernatural strength, promotion, financial blessings and divine protection.

I challenge you to become physically fit today. What are you blessed with? I am blessed with _____.

Remember, do not ask the Lord to guide your footsteps if you are not willing to move your feet.

Leslie V. Corbin

Thank you, Andrea L. Jackson and Leslie V. Corbin for your powerful testimonies.

Let's take this a little bit further. The Center for Disease Control states that adults need two hours and thirty minutes (150 minutes) of moderate-intensity aerobic activity (i.e., brisk walking) every week and two or more days of muscle-strengthening activities a week (legs, hips, back, abdomen, chest, shoulders and arms) to maintain good health. This will do the following:

Control Your Weight

Are you looking to get to or stay at a healthy weight? Both diet and physical activity play a critical role in controlling your weight. You gain weight when the calories you burn, including those burned during physical activity, are less than the calories you eat or drink. When it comes to weight management, people vary greatly in how much physical activity they need. You may need to be more active than others to achieve or maintain a healthy weight.

To maintain your weight: Work your way up to 150 minutes of moderate-intensity aerobic activity, 75 minutes of vigorous-intensity aerobic activity, or an equivalent mix of the two each week. Strong scientific evidence shows that physical activity can help you maintain your weight over time. However, the exact amount of physical activity needed to do this is not clear since it varies greatly from person to person. It is possible that you may need to do more than the equivalent of 150 minutes of moderate-intensity activity a week to maintain your weight.

To lose weight and keep it off: You will need a high amount of physical activity unless you also adjust your diet and reduce the amount of calories you are eating and drinking. Getting to and staying at a healthy weight requires both regular physical activity and a healthy eating plan. The CDC has some great tools and information about nutrition, physical activity and weight loss.

Reduce Your Risk of Cardiovascular Disease

Heart disease and stroke are two of the leading causes of death in the United States. But following the Guidelines and getting at least 150 minutes a week (two hours and thirty minutes) of moderate-intensity aerobic activity can put you at a lower risk for these diseases. You can reduce your risk even further with more physical activity. Regular physical activity can also lower your blood pressure and improve your cholesterol levels.

Reduce your risk of Type 2 Diabetes and Metabolic Syndrome

Regular physical activity can reduce your risk of developing type 2 diabetes and metabolic syndrome. Metabolic syndrome is a condition in which you have some combination of too much fat around the waist, high blood pressure, low HDL cholesterol, high triglycerides, or high blood sugar. Research shows that lower rates of these conditions are seen with 120 to 150 minutes (2 hours to 2 hours and 30 minutes) a week of at least moderate-intensity aerobic activity. The more physical activity you do, the lower your risk will be.

Do you already have type 2 diabetes? Regular physical activity can help control your blood glucose levels.

Reduce Your Risk of Some Cancers

Being physically active lowers your risk for two types of cancer: colon and breast. Research shows that:

- Physically active people have a lower risk of colon cancer than do people who are not active.

- Physically active women have a lower risk of breast cancer than do people who are not active.

Reduce your risk of endometrial and lung cancer. Although the research is not yet final, some findings suggest that your risk of endometrial cancer and lung cancer may be lower if you get regular physical activity compared to people who are not active.

Improve your quality of life. If you are a cancer survivor, research shows that getting regular physical activity not only helps give you a better quality of life, but also improves your physical fitness.

Strengthen Your Bones and Muscles

As you age, it is important to protect your bones, joints and muscles. Not only do they support your body and help you move, but keeping bones, joints and muscles healthy can help ensure that you are able to do your daily activities and be physically active. Research shows that doing **aerobic, muscle-strengthening and bone-strengthening physical activity** of at least a moderately-intense level **can slow the loss of bone density** that comes with age.

Hip fracture is a serious health condition that can have life-changing negative effects, especially if you are an older adult. But research shows that people who do 120 to 300 minutes of at least moderate-intensity aerobic activity each week have a lower risk of hip fracture.

Regular physical activity helps with arthritis and other conditions affecting the joints. If you have arthritis, research shows that doing 130 to 150 (two hours and ten minutes to two hours and thirty minutes) a week of moderate-intensity, low-impact aerobic activity can, not only improve your ability to manage pain and do everyday tasks, but it can also make your quality of life better.

Build strong, healthy muscles. Muscle-strengthening activities can help you increase or maintain your muscle mass and strength. Slowly increasing the amount of weight and number of repetitions you do will give you even more benefits, no matter your age.

Improve Your Mental Health and Mood

Regular physical activity can help keep your thinking, learning, and judgment skills sharp as you age. It can also reduce your risk of depression and may help you sleep better. Research has shown that doing aerobic or a mix of aerobic and muscle-strengthening activities three to five times a week for thirty to sixty minutes can give you these mental health benefits. Some scientific evidence has also shown that even lower levels of physical activity can be beneficial.

Improve Your Ability to do
Daily Activities and Prevent Falls

A functional limitation is a loss of the ability to do everyday activities such as climbing stairs, grocery shopping, or playing with your grandchildren.

How does this relate to physical activity? If you are a physically active middle-aged or older adult, you have a lower risk of functional limitations than people who are inactive.

Do you already have trouble doing some of your everyday activities? Aerobic and muscle-strengthening activities can help improve your ability to do these types of tasks.

Are you an older adult who is at risk for falls? Research shows that doing **balance** and **muscle-strengthening activities** each week along with **moderate-intensity aerobic activity**, like brisk walking, can help reduce your risk of falling.

Increase Your Chances of Living Longer

Science shows that physical activity can reduce your risk of dying early from the leading causes of death, like heart disease and some cancers. This is remarkable in two ways:

1. Only a few lifestyle choices have as large an impact on your health as physical activity. People who are physically active for about seven hours a week have a forty percent lower risk of dying early than those who are active for less than thirty minutes a week.

2. You do not have to do high amounts of activity or vigorous-intensity activity to reduce your risk of premature death. You can put yourself at lower risk of dying early by doing at least 150 minutes a week of moderate-intensity aerobic activity.

Everyone can gain the health benefits of physical activity - age, ethnicity, shape or size do not matter.

What a small price to pay for a long healthy life. So as you can see, exercise, eating right and the proper rest plays a big part in prospering physically. Let's do our part guys so that God can continue to do His part. I decided that I wanted to be here to see my daughter get married and have an opportunity to spoil my grandchildren. My love for my child and her future is very important to me. I realized that my habits of eating wrong and not working out did not line up with my heart. If I love my family like I say I do then I would be willing to make the necessary changes to live longer. Therefore, I press forward with all my might to hit the desired goals physically. Won't you join me?

I wish for you nothing but prosperity in this area so that we can be all that God has called us to be while on this earth.

God Bless you and much success to you and your family.

Chapter V Journal Pages

Answer the following questions for Physical Prosperity.

1.   On a scale of 1 to 5, how strong are you in this area?

_____

_____

_____

_____

_____

_____

2.   What are some of the things you are doing to grow in this area?

_____

_____

_____

_____

_____

_____

3.   How often do you evaluate your growth in this area?

_____

_____

_____

_____

_____

_____

4. How strong are the people around you in this area?

_____

_____

_____

_____

_____

_____

5. Who is your mentor in this area and how often do you talk to them?

_____

_____

_____

_____

_____

6. What is your personal mission statement?

_____

_____

_____

_____

_____

_____

_____

_____

Chapter VI: Financial Prosperity

There were times when I did not know any better that I wanted to jump straight to this area and prosper beyond my wildest imagination. Too often, we associate hardship and unhappiness with lack of money, therefore we rationalize that the cure to my hardship and unhappiness must be money. Now that I have matured, I understand clearly that just prospering financially will not only hurt you, it can actually kill you. You may have heard of people with financial freedom committing suicide, or getting hooked on drugs and asked yourself why. A common statement is, "If I had the money that person has I would not do that." Well my friend, it is possible that you would. If one is empty spiritually, mentally weak, associations are negative, and physical energy is negative then the financial will be off as well. If they have money they will use it as a tool of destruction. If they do not have money they will use whatever they get a hold of as a tool of destruction. Yes it actually works both ways.

I grew up in a very loving family and my parents worked very hard to provide a comfortable life for their children. Now it was nine of us so it was not an easy task. My dad was a true provider and if it took three jobs to make sure his family had a roof over their heads and food to eat then he was willing to do it. We did not have a lot of material wealth but we carried ourselves so well that people always thought we had so much more. My mom kept her children very clean. The house was always spotless and my parents could make a meal smell and look so good, even if it was just a pot of beans. If I could be half the woman my mom is I will be a powerful lady. What a strong support system and family structure my parents had then and still have today.

Well, having all that love did not take away from the fact that financially we lived in lack. My dad made enough to sustain the household and at times there was nothing left, but God! God always kept us.

3 John 1:2

*Beloved, I wish above all things that thou mayest **prosper** and be in health, even as thy **soul prosper**eth.*

We should have money but, if we are empty inside, do not know who and whose we are, have low self esteem, attach to the wrong people, are out of shape inwardly and outwardly then money will only cause us to jump over a bridge. Nevertheless, we must understand how money works.

Unfortunately, the school system is not teaching us the principles of money and our students are graduating with no knowledge of how to manage a checkbook. Our parents, at times, teach us what they know and they mean well but many times their knowledge base is limited as well. So what do we do?

Well, I remember interviewing one of my many mentors and I asked him, "What are the differences between the people that have and the have nots." He made it very clear that the only difference between the rich and the poor is the way they think. The mindset plays a major part in how millionaires/successful people accomplish their wealth. God is not a respecter of persons, meaning He would never say let this group of people win in life and the other group fail. He gave us all the same formula to wealth.

Seed + Time = Harvest

If you plant the right seeds in due season you will reap a harvest. The issue is that the poor/middle income families do not know how and/or what seeds to plant. I asked the same mentor, "How does one learn what, where and how to plant those seeds." He said, "Lisa, the number one issue with middle income/ poor people is they won't go to the meetings." I was like huh? He said, "There are great opportunities going on right here in my state that would afford folks the funds needed to fund their businesses. There are centers of influencers all around, willing to coach folks into the mindset needed to be independent and yet folks won't seek the wisdom. They are so exhausted from giving the boss man the best hours of their day that when it comes time for them to learn what successful people know they get sleepy. Therefore, they stay in bondage and never succeed."

He said he always made money because his father taught him how to be an owner not a renter. You see a job only allows you to rent an income but a business allows you to own an income. People stay under that corporate system of bondage so long that they start to accept it as their **destiny or fate**. That system was not designed for us to be independent. It was designed to give us enough money to hopefully keep a roof over our heads and return on Monday. It reminds me of a movie that came out in 1994 called, The Shawshank Redemption. It had some profound quotes in it but this one stood out. "These walls are kind of funny. First you hate 'em, then you get used to 'em; enough time passes, gets so you dependent on them. That's institutionalized. They send you here for life, that's exactly what they take. The part that counts, anyways."

Folks have learned how to live in bondage so well that they think it is all God has for them in their life. It is actually sad to watch. I remember hosting a time management workshop for an agency and one of the attendees said that she had been in her current position for twenty plus years and she has hated every year. Why did she stay there? It is the mindset. She truly does not know how to think any differently. She REALLY needs to go to the meetings. That statement was so profound for me because I attribute all my success to the fact that I go to the meetings. I started thinking and believing in myself more. I started walking different and thinking different and talking different because I went to the meetings.

There must be a renewing of the mind to change your life financially. You cannot keep doing the same thing and get a different result. If $60,000 did not pay the bills last year my friend, it will not pay the bills this year. In the corporate system, as employees, your income is decided for you. An employee is not given a choice of income. The $60,000 is what you are given in exchange for your work. However, as a business OWNER you have a say in your income.

Am I saying that everybody should be a business owner, NO. It would be nice but the fact is somebody needs to be a doctor, a police officer, a dentist, a fire fighter, a teacher and most importantly a soldier. I appreciate so much all that these guys do to make my and so many other lives better. I do believe that, because of the limited income potential in some of these positions, one needs a money coach to help them stay accountable – to achieve their goals.

Now you have a few financial guru's out there who get rich selling you their tapes, books and kits. I am not talking about them. It is a good read but the fact is if one is not held accountable to change then its likely not to happen. Very few people are disciplined enough to do it themselves. Yes an accountability coach has helped me to achieve many of my goals in life. When left to lean on my own understanding I mess up. Thanks to my mentors I have a clear concise mental picture of where I am going and if I get off track I have someone to call me out and bring me back. I am not immature in this area. I am not high maintenance, but I do like the idea that somebody cares about my achievements in all areas of prosperity.

How do you start?

I believe the foundation has to be laid properly. In the Bible it talks about giving 10% of all earnings back to God. You will notice if you study successful people they give away half of their wealth to causes they believe in and as a result their money keeps making money. The rich truly do get richer. Being a Christian and believing in scripture I know that I cannot break the bondage of poverty if I am stealing from the kingdom of God.

In my household I taught my daughter the 10-10-80 rule. 10% to tithes, 10% to pay me and 80% to everything else. The issue within so many households is 100% plus goes to everything else. People are living beyond their means and as a result it affects their relationships, their physical, their mental and their self esteem. Does this mean if they have money these areas will not be affected? Not at all. It just means that it is one less area that you have to work on. I have met people who are strong in three of the five areas. They just needed to know what else was missing. So, evaluating yourself using all five areas is such a great frame of reference.

There are seven levels that one must address in order to build a strong financial house. I will address those levels after I talk about the importance of a strong foundation. I am told that a house foundation serves a threefold purposes.

- It lifts your house above the ground;

- It keeps out cold and moisture; and

- It holds your house steady even when the earth surrounding it is prone to movement.

Wow! Isn't that powerful? The foundation for building a **strong financial house** is tithing. If I adhere to this principle, I will be lifted above my debts, there will be no damage to my bank accounts and when that thing called life hits and everything around me is falling apart, I will remain steady because I abide by the principle of giving God his 10%. I like the sound of that.

Breaking Covenant by Withholding Tithes

Malachi 3:6-12

6 *"I the LORD do not change. So you, the descendants of Jacob, are not destroyed.*

7 *Ever since the time of your ancestors you have turned away from my decrees and have not kept them. Return to me, and I will return to you," says the LORD Almighty. "But you ask, 'How are we to return?'*

8 *"Will a mere mortal rob God? Yet you rob me. "But you ask, 'How are we robbing you?' "In tithes and offerings.*

9 *You are under a curse—your whole nation— because you are robbing me.*

10 *Bring the whole tithe into the storehouse, that there may be food in my house. Test me in this," says the LORD Almighty, "and see if I will not throw open the floodgates of heaven and pour out so much blessing that there will not be room enough to store it.*

11 *I will prevent pests from devouring your crops, and the vines in your fields will not drop their fruit before it is ripe," says the LORD Almighty.*

12 *"Then all the nations will call you blessed, for yours will be a delightful land," says the LORD Almighty.*

I know this to be real in my life. I have not always abided by this principle and I certainly saw a difference in my income and growth. I trust God with the 10%. It is truly amazing to me that 10% is all He requires of us. I mean the department store credit cards want 24%, Visa wants 18% and God only wants 10%. What a mighty God we serve. I also noticed that even the nonbelievers abide by this principle. This principle holds true whether one is a believer or not. Most successful people donate much more than 10% to charity and as a result of that the rich truly do get richer. If you are a member of a church, you have an obligation to tithe that 10% in the storehouse (church home).

When we have proclaimed Jesus in our life, our offerings, our tithe, all that we have has the life of God in it. Place any portion of that which we have into something and the result will be that the life of God will cause more life!

The word of the Lord says:

> "'And I will rebuke the devourer for your sakes,
> So that he will not destroy the fruit of your
> ground, Nor shall the vine fail to bear fruit for
> you in the field,' Says the LORD of hosts."
> (Malachi 3:11, NKJV)

A strong foundation holds it all together. Let's talk about what is happening in the average household today. According to "The Survey of Consumer Payment Choice," Federal Reserve Bank Boston 2010, the average household has 3.5 credit cards with an average balance of $15,956 or more. The debt for student loans is higher than the debt for war. The average household only has $50,000 worth of life insurance coverage on the breadwinner in their household. Not only does one not know their needs at retirement, but if one of the breadwinners were to ever need assistance due to illness or physical ailments, the retirement accounts would be depleted because there is no protection on the retirement. Foreclosures are at an all time high and not necessarily because one was just laid off, but because the buyers made an emotional decision and bought too much of a house. I say it again; accountability would have helped many to make a more informed decision about their purchases and their financial plans.

The financial industry intrigues me a lot. Just understanding how money works has helped me to make better decisions for my family and me. I know more now than ever because I do not only go to the meetings, I now run the meetings.

Seventeen years ago, long before I met my current mentors, I started attending meetings where a team of people were being trained on how to market financial solutions. They made learning so much fun. God knows I needed that humor because I knew nothing about this industry prior to attending the meeting. I researched the suggestions given and it all turned out to be accurate.

I became even more involved at that time. I decided to obtain my license with the state of Maryland so that I could be like the people I met with weekly. I gained so much wisdom about money principles that I could not keep it to myself. The more I went to the meeting the more my mindset was changing to believe I could really one day be a business owner. Making a decision to become part of this company was one of the best decisions I made. With much research and training I found their solutions and philosophy to be sound and practical. It was rather annoying to know that the principles I was being taught had been around for years and was rather simple but the industry and a number of companies benefited from holding sound truths from us.

I developed a crusade to teach my family and friends the truth. God started to reveal even more truths to me as I continued to allow the leadership to develop me and sow positive seeds into me. I began to believe in myself and eventually I desired to be a major player in this company. I was no longer satisfied with being average and ordinary. I wanted more and I realized that I determined my self worth, not a boss or HR. I was really going to teach people worldwide how to cure a financial cancer. My clients would not be just a number to me but someone I could sincerely help by teaching them how to enhance their current plan or simply how to put a plan together.

I cannot begin to explain how it felt when I helped a family put together a debt freedom plan or taught them how to plan for their children's education. I taught them how to determine their FIN#, Financial Independence Number. They had never heard that term before. It makes sense considering too many are retiring broke in our country. I will never forget after sitting down with a family and educating them on these sound principles, they told me that they were praying for help but did not know where to go to get it. They thanked me over and over because God had answered their prayers through me. I was so excited that night that I could not sleep.

Could God really be using me as a vessel to answer prayers? I started marketing for a company that did not require me to lie, cheat or steal. I could tell the truth and be proud about it. The mission statement alone is powerful. We help families become properly protected, debt free and financially independent. My oh my, was it possible to achieve all three of these things at the same time, and was it possible for me? It was so powerful to me that I told and continue to tell many about the concepts. Knowledge is powerful only when applied so I started servicing my clients after making sure they were thoroughly educated on these sound principles. I did not mind folks researching the principles because they were accurate and doable. What an experience I have been on for years with this company. As a licensed representative, I am often solicited to join other companies that market financial products and I tell you guys I choose only this company. I absolutely refuse to market products that are taking advantage of the client only to make the company a profit. I believe in the product, the philosophy and the mission statement of this company.

Okay, I hear you. To what company are you referring? The name of the company is Primerica. Primerica is a company of integrity, character and a proven track record. I believe this is the only company that takes the time to teach and implement a game plan to help middle-income families achieve the goals they have for their families.

Primerica is the largest independent financial services marketing organization in North America. They are a member of the New York Stock Exchange (PRI). Greater than two million clients maintain investment accounts with them. Over 4.3 million lives are insured through this company. The main focus is to teach people how money works so they can make informed decisions about how to manage their finances. I tell my clients that everything comes with instructions, but that paycheck. If you purchase a toaster it has instructions but that paycheck, no instructions. On payday it is temporary millionaire's day. Everybody goes out to lunch on payday.

One must know how to build a strong financial house. We take great pride in educating you on all levels and then having the staff available to service you on those seven levels. The seven levels are Income Protection, Emergency Fund, Asset Management, Debt Management, Budgeting, Education/Retirement Accounts, and yes, Goals and Dreams Accounts.

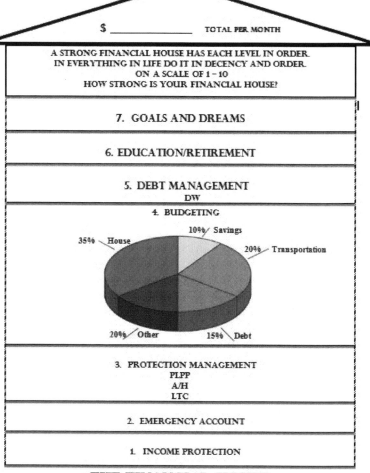

$ _____ TOTAL PER MONTH

A STRONG FINANCIAL HOUSE HAS EACH LEVEL IN ORDER.
IN EVERYTHING IN LIFE DO IT IN DECENCY AND ORDER.
ON A SCALE OF 1 – 10
HOW STRONG IS YOUR FINANCIAL HOUSE?

7. GOALS AND DREAMS

6. EDUCATION/RETIREMENT

5. DEBT MANAGEMENT
DW

4. BUDGETING

10% Savings
35% House
20% Transportation
20% Other
15% Debt

3. PROTECTION MANAGEMENT
PLPP
A/H
LTC

2. EMERGENCY ACCOUNT

1. INCOME PROTECTION

THE FINANCIAL HOUSE

We must have a roadmap in place for our finances. If not we could definitely get lost. Above is a visual of what the levels are and gaining the knowledge to learn how each level complements the other is very important.

When my clients see this guideline they feel a sense of relief because finally somebody simplified it to a point they can understand and follow.

Income Protection – If you ask most people what their biggest or most important asset is they would say their house. Actually, unless you are financially independent and your house is paying you, it is not your biggest asset. For most their biggest asset is their ability to earn income. We must protect our income so that our family can have the same standard of living or greater at our death.

Emergency Account – Can you remember how much your last emergency cost you? Yes we must put aside cash for emergencies and stop relying on credit cards to take care of them. My clients put aside an identified amount monthly to achieve a goal of three to six months of household expenses saved.

The first two levels are very important and will ensure that levels 3 through 7 happen whether they are alive or not. I can show you how to be debt free and how to retire in decency and order, but I cannot promise you tomorrow. Unfortunately, the fact remains that somebody will die and there will be an emergency.

Protection Management – Our assets, like our homes and cars, must be properly protected. What exactly does that mean and how do I know if I am overpaying? I address this issue for my clients. We also need to understand the importance of Long Term Care. Putting protection on your retirement is key. Do you have a Will or Estate Plan? It is very important to understand how these documents work and why they are necessary.

Budgeting – No, we did not make this a level by mistake. It is essential that you understand the difference between a debt and an expense. I find that the average household wastes $200 to $500 a month. Yes, even with the economy we are in today. One area is entertainment. They are spending $300 to $500 in groceries and another $200 in restaurants. Oh yes, it is true.

Debt Management – Like I stated before, folks emergency money is a credit card now. The credit card companies love you so much that they allow you to pick your own background. If only making a minimum payment, it can take 39 years to payoff a $3000 credit card. The minimum required payment does not apply a large enough amount to the principle to lower it by any significance.

Education Plan – Let's put something away for our children. Often folks spend more on clothes and holiday gifts than they do on their future. Learn how to save and where.

Retirement Plan – What is your FIN number? Is your current plan allocated properly? We must educate ourselves on this area. You need to know what plans will be suited to your needs at retirement.

Goals and Dream – I do not just want to teach my clients how to die in decency but how to live as well. Enjoy your life, go somewhere. Dream again, but plan for it. Success is by design, not by default. Design your victories. Travel the beaches of the world. Save monthly in your accounts

> *Habakkuk 2:1-3*
>
> *¹ will stand upon my watch, and set me upon the tower, and will watch to see what he will say unto me, and what I shall answer when I am reproved.*
>
> *² And the LORD answered me, and said, Write the vision, and make it plain upon tables, that he may run that readeth it.*

3 For the vision is yet for an appointed time, but at the end it shall speak, and not lie: though it tarry, wait for it; because it will surely come, it will not tarry.

There must be a written plan. The family, meaning both spouses and the children, need to understand it. Like the scripture says, the vision is for an appointed time and though it may tarry, it will surely come. Much success to you and your family.

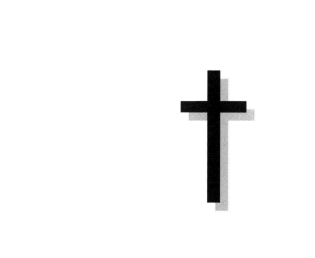

Chapter VI Journal Pages

Answer the following questions for Financial Prosperity.

1. On a scale of 1 to 5, how strong are you in this area?

_____

_____

_____

_____

_____

_____

2. What are some of the things you are doing to grow in this area?

_____

_____

_____

_____

_____

3. How often do you evaluate your growth in this area?

_____

_____

_____

_____

_____

_____

4. How strong are the people around you in this area?

_____

_____

_____

_____

_____

_____

5. Who is your mentor in this area and how often do you talk to them?

_____

_____

_____

_____

_____

_____

6. What is your personal mission statement?

_____

_____

_____

_____

_____

_____

_____

_____

Chapter VII: My JOB Experience

Thank you so much for allowing me to share my life with you. Writing this book has been such a great experience and I promise you I am first partaker of what has come out of my mouth and heart. I started writing this book last year (2011) and in the beginning I was overjoyed at the thought of finishing a book. It is my greatest desire that one is touched and inspired to grow in these five areas and realize an Extreme MakeOver.

Have I perfected these areas, absolutely not. I still have room for much growth. I can say God made sure I understood the power behind these five areas just in time.

I remember reading the book of JOB in the Bible. JOB was a blameless and upright man of God. He was so devoted to God and his family. He was a successful man, loved by many. One day Satan was looking for something to do and because God knew JOB's heart, he allowed Satan to test JOB. After much loss and turmoil JOB prevailed.

I am not nearly as flawless as JOB but I had what I would call my JOB experience in 2011. In March, I was attending an African American Leadership Conference in Atlanta, Georgia. After eating lunch one day I got really sick. I went to the doctor and after a quick checkup they released me with a prescription for pain pills. I returned home after missing some of the conference and things got better, the pain went away. April 2011, I returned to Atlanta, GA again to celebrate my daughter's birthday and got sick again. By that time I was thinking something was wrong with Georgia, because surely there is nothing wrong with me. It was worse the second time so as soon as I returned to Baltimore I went straight to the emergency room. After an all night visit, I was told to see my Primary Care Doctor.

Two days later I went to see my doctor and he did a biopsy because he noticed some unusual looking cells. I was told that the results would return in a couple of days but much to my surprise, the results returned the next day. I received a call from the nurse asking me to come to the office and bring a family member with me.

"Okay, sure, I'll be right there," was my response. I called my cousin to go with me but because I did not want her to hear or see me weak, I told her to come a half hour after my appointment. I then did the next best thing and I texted my mentor/friend and asked him to pray for me because I was very weak. Like the friend he is, he called as soon as he got the text and asked me what was going on. I told him the exact words I got from the nurse and he talked to me while I cried from an overwhelming fear of bad news. You do not get a call like that only to say you are healthy. He gave me a set of instructions and prayed my strength in the Lord. I tell you, when the storm of life hits, you better know the right phone call to make. I will never forget how my mind was racing while I was driving to the doctor's office. But like my mentor instructed, I had gospel music playing and I was talking to God. He is my strength, my source, my provider. The doctor called me into his office and proceeded to tell me that the lab called right away and stated that my biopsy return showing that I had cervical cancer. I looked at him like he was an alien. WHAT? Where did that come from? Things like that do not happen to me.

Job 1:9 – 11

⁹ "Does Job fear God for nothing?" Satan replied.

¹⁰ "Have you not put a hedge around him and his household and everything he has? You have blessed the work of his hands, so that his flocks and herds are spread throughout the land.

¹¹ But now stretch out your hand and strike everything he has, and he will surely curse you to your face."

Prayer is so awesome. At that time, my life was going so well. The fruits of my prayers were evident. I was building a new team of leaders and my activity had increased. I was travelling and having fun. Then all of a sudden, much like JOB, it was like the enemy said to God, "Let me try her and see how much she loves you." JOB did not do anything to deserve his fate. I was not flawless like JOB, but man I tried hard to be upright and spread the love of God.

I got that diagnosis and went straight to a hotel and checked in because I did not want anyone to see me. I called my mentor/friend, Mike Evans, and gave him the news as he requested and I cried with a pain I had never felt before. He talked me through it as best he could. He immediately put me on a plan of attack. "It's time for us to fight Lisa. We will speak nothing but life into the atmosphere."

Again I ask, who do you call when life gets tough and you are so low you cannot see or get up? Well, I tell you I called the right people. I checked into the hotel and I called my best friend of 25 years and told her. Leslie and I have always been able to talk about anything. We do not judge each other and we support each other. She is my sister. My circle of friends is broad I must say. I am private though so I did not tell everyone right away. It was a long night at the hotel and I cried on and off the entire night. It was so unbelievable to me. My doctor hugged me because he did not know what to say. I was always on time for my checkups and there had been no sign of cervical cancer three months prior. It seemed to appear out of nowhere.

From that point on I was getting sicker and sicker. I could not sleep at night and my energy was zapped. I did everything I could to hide the pain and fear. I continued to go on appointments and I even took a five hour drive to North Carolina to conduct a few appointments. I could not bring myself to tell my family because I did not want to hurt them with such news. We had been through this already. My niece was diagnosed with Ovarian Cancer at age 15. We were in total awe over that situation. We were not ready for that storm and God knows they were not ready for mine. My immediate thoughts were, "I am the strong one, the go-to one, the leader, the encourager, the motivator, the confidante and the provider. Who's going to take care of my family? There is no time for this because I have people to take care of."

My Spiritual Prosperity area had to kick in overdrive. My belief system had to be in order. I was in for one of the biggest challenges of my life.

I was referred to a Specialist at Mercy Hospital in Baltimore, Maryland. Dr. Im. He examined me and confirmed the diagnosis. He said something to me that gave me some well needed comfort. "Lisa, God is going to perform the surgery and He will use my hands." Oh my, I love Dr. Im. That was the best statement he could have made at that time. One of my best friends, my confidante, my cousin was with me every step of the way. I am forever grateful for Andrea Jackson for her undying love and respect. She has made me such a better person. One of the best Mentees one can ask. (Relationship Prosperity) Suddenly she was placed in a Mentor role in my life. I relied so much on her strength and wisdom. She questioned the doctors. She oversaw my business, went on many doctor appointments with me and kept my circle of prayer warriors informed of my status.

I still could not find the strength to tell my family and my daughter who resides in Georgia. So I hid my pain and diagnosis for awhile. I got sicker and sicker and my mom kept asking me what was going on. The words would not come out my mouth. I love her, I could not bring worry to her. Then the call came from Mike.

"Lisa, I need you to tell your family."

"Mike I am not ready."

"Lisa I admire your strength, even in your distress you are still protecting others. Tell your family and tell your leaders/business partners now."

Because of my loyalty and respect for leadership, Mike knew if he made a request I would adhere to it. I called my sister and I told her while she was at work and I was sitting in the car. That was not a smart move, but I promise you I was not thinking correctly during that time. I asked her not to tell the family members just yet. I called a meeting with the office leaders and I told them at breakfast. I demanded strength, no tears – and success. I did not want to see anyone cry.

It was getting closer to the surgery day and I needed to tell my parents, my daughter and siblings. I requested that my sister Bridget tell them but no one was to call me crying and sad. I could not deal with that. I did not want to discuss it. It was very difficult for me to allow them to see me weak. I do not know if that is pride or protection. They granted me my wish and remained very calm when I came around and did not ask me any questions. My good friends in Georgia took care of my daughter and told her for me. She called crying and came home to be by my side the entire time.

Finally, the day for surgery had arrived and thank God because it was too painful to deal with the agony. The pain was horrendous. It is hard to explain. It was worse than the pain of childbearing. I had never been so sick in my life. I wish that experience on no one. There were many sleepless nights and plenty of tears. I could not eat, sleep and at times I could not walk. I could relate to JOB when he said in JOB 6:11-13:

> 11 *"What strength do I have, that I should still hope?*
>
> *What prospects, that I should be patient?*
>
> 12 *Do I have the strength of stone? Is my flesh bronze?*

13 Do I have any power to help myself, now that success has been driven from me?

I begged my doctor to take me into surgery before the scheduled date because I was in so much pain. I made several visits to the emergency room and it was just time. He honored my request and moved up the scheduled surgery. That day my parents, sister, Bridgett, best friends Leslie and Andrea, and I went in for preparation for surgery. I went through every emotion – fear, nervousness, sickness and weakness. It was a dreadful day.

When they wheeled me into the surgery room and I felt the cold and saw all the steel tables and tools I was petrified. I said to God, "I am not sure if I am going to make it out of here alive." I said, "Lord I am so glad you saved me. I know to be absent from the body is to be present with the Lord. I submit my spirit unto thee." I did not expect to live. My mental prosperity was weak.

Can somebody say "BUT GOD." When I awoke in the recovery room I was in shock. I saw my parents and my sister and I said, "Am I living?" I am alive. I was really surprised. That surgery room was so scary that I did not think anybody made it out of there alive. The last thing I could remember was the anesthesiologist asking me what was I going to do after the surgery and I said, "Go to Hawaii."

My thoughts were all over the place. I was thinking things like, "Now that the surgery is over and I am still alive, all I have to do is recover for about three days and get back to work." After all, business is increasing and I am back on track. It did not quite happen that fast. I was released from the hospital in three days. I thought it would be another couple of days but much to my surprise, I got sick again. The pain returned, the fever was elevated, I got weak and could not sleep. "What is this?" I had the surgery. The cancer was gone. Why was I so sick? I knew I was sick and that my fever had to be about 100 degrees so I asked my sister to take me to the hospital at three o'clock in the morning.

While going through that experience I knew I had to listen to the right music, so I played gospel music and set the atmosphere. I talked to spiritually and mentally strong friends who sowed seeds of encouragement into me. They never let me have a pity party; and, I prayed scriptures of healing throughout my day. I talked to God so much and I trusted Him even in my pain. I trusted my Lord and Savior so much.

It got worse though. I became so sick and was admitted into the hospital again. I had a fever of 105 degrees and I was in so much pain, again. The fever was an indication that there was an infection in my body. Because the doctor had removed so many lymph nodes, the fluids that normally flow through those nodes had formed into a cyst. It required a procedure that included placing a catheter within the cyst, and attaching tubing to drain the fluid into a vacuum bottle. I felt like it had to be a nightmare because none of it made sense from beginning to end.

I had to stay in the hospital for over a week and during that time I had to get two blood transfusions and scan after scan of the infected area. I was worn out by then and my mental prosperity was weak. It sank further and further because it got worse. I could barely walk, I was tired and the pain was terrible. The nurses checked my vitals every thirty minutes. I would not tell them I was in pain because I did not want to take the pain pills, so I suffered until they caught on.

The nurse asked, "Ms. Jones are you in pain?"

With a weak voice I replied, "No."

"Ms. Jones I believe you are in pain because your pressure is really high. If you do not tell us the truth we will assume you have an illness that is not necessarily there, like high blood pressure."

Well by then I did not want to hear another diagnosis so I admitted that I was paranoid about taking pain pills because I feared getting addicted. She thought that was so funny because most patients beg for pain medicine and I was refusing it.

"Ms. Jones you will not get addicted, my God you just had surgery two weeks ago. The medicine will help you with pain and infection."

I was going through so much mentally that I did not know what to believe. I was a nice patient but a stubborn one. Believe it or not to that point I still had not accepted the fact that I was sick. I know it sounds crazy but I felt like the doctors and nurses had the issues because I was fine and it was all a mistake and they needed to give me the one pill to stop everything and let me go home. It was such a mental battle for me. I am used to being in control and taking care of myself. I am used to serving others not being served. I was made humble for sure.

I remember wanting to go home. I begged them to let me go home. I was getting better so why stay there. They asked that I walk the hallway three times a day and eat my food. Well I would walk four times a day and I still could not eat. I would wrap the food in napkins and throw it away and pretend I ate it. That was terrible I know, but I wanted to go home. They released me and guess what? I got sick again. During one week my whole body was itching so bad I was in agony. Then one week my eyes got bloodshot red and I could not see. Then I could not walk. I had to sit in a chair to get some relief because lying in my bed was painful. I went from my bedroom at mom's house to the hospital regularly. My JOB experience kicked in again and Satan was feeding me these thoughts:

Job 2:9-10

9 His wife said to him, "Are you still maintaining your integrity? Curse God and die!"

10 He replied, "You are talking like a foolish[b] woman. Shall we accept good from God, and not trouble?"

The attack on my mental was so strong and the enemy wanted my life so bad. I did not understand it all then, but I know without a shadow of doubt if I did not have a relationship and I mean an intimate relationship with Christ I would have gone into a deep depression.

The doctor visits were often and very costly. By that time I was not only dealing with pain but then stress kicked in. My business was slacking due to lack of leadership. My income had decreased dramatically and my confidence was shot. I could not see myself ever returning to my business again or speaking before an audience again. I lost the vision. The enemy was starting to get the best of me. One reason I held on was for my daughter. She stayed in the hospital with me every night. I felt so bad for her. She slept in an uncomfortable chair every single night. She bathed me and she fed me. My God! My twenty-two year old daughter was my caretaker. How could I do this to her?

You see, I felt like I caused this illness and had inconvenienced everybody who loved me. I am a person who takes ownership for my mistakes and I thought I had done this to myself. I did not blame God or family or friends. I blamed me. I wanted nothing from anybody but prayer. I would ask my warriors to just pray for me. That was the most meaningful thing that anyone could do at that time. My parents would sit for hours in the hospital with me. My siblings were there, my two-mom Vernell Price was there, and my selected group of friends whom I allowed to come were there. I did not want many to see me because I looked so bad and I did not want them to remember me that way. So I kept many away and would not talk to them on the phone. Some were offended but I had to deal with it the best way I knew how. It was truly not about them, it was about me.

My JOB experience came on again. I was searching for the words to describe how I was feeling and how low I had gotten and in JOB 3:20-26 he said to God:

20 *"Why is light given to those in misery, and life to the bitter of soul,*

21 *to those who long for death that does not come, who search for it more than for hidden treasure,*

22 *who are filled with gladness and rejoice when they reach the grave?*

23 *Why is life given to a man whose way is hidden, whom God has hedged in?*

24 *For sighing has become my daily food; my groans pour out like water.*

25 *What I feared has come upon me; what I dreaded has happened to me.*

26 *I have no peace, no quietness; I have no rest, but only turmoil.*

I told God I would rather die than live a life of illness and pain. I was so sick and low. I had entered into a dark place and I was drowning. It brings tears to my eyes to think of how low I had descended. The enemy wanted me to curse God. Not me, I would never curse God, but I did question myself and said, "There is something I must have done to cause this and God I repent and I beg for forgiveness. Please let me die so I can feel better."

I then was told that I had to do treatment. Radiation to be exact and I was not happy about that. For twenty-five weeks I had to lay on that steel cold table and let a machine shoot rays into my body, five days a week. I was in disbelief. I had the surgery; the cancer was gone, what else did they want from me?

I was told radiation would be a breeze. "It is not as bad as chemo so you will be fine." Of course, that was not true. I got so sick from the radiation that I lost control over some functions of my body. I could not hold food on my stomach and I was weak. There was barely enough energy to get up in the mornings. Here I was in the fourth month since the diagnosis and I was still sick. You need to understand, for an action person who is always on the move it was torture.

Week after week I fussed, kicked, hollered and screamed, "Please release me from this treatment." I told the doctor that this was a waste of my time and "If I was not doing this treatment I would have been better by now." I was truly angry. I am not a nasty person so I would never treat anybody wrong. I always showed respect but the doctor knew I was not happy about the situation. I would have talks with Dr. Ottinger about how the procedures she would perform on me had to be modified so that the patient would not be so uncomfortable.

I did my motivational speeches to the doctor and she would laugh at me. I still had a little sense of humor in my dry place. After several weeks of treatment, I started to see the same patients every day. They were there for treatment for different types of cancer. Most of the women had breast cancer and they were all bald. They were not only getting radiation treatment but chemo as well. I started feeling like, "Lisa you are such a weak individual. How dare you complain after seeing what these ladies are going through. I mean they have cancer and you are complaining because of a little pain."

Believe it or not I still did not accept the fact that I had cancer, until one day I was asked if I was a cancer survivor. I said, "No."

I was then asked if I was getting treatment and I said, "Yes."

"For what?"

"Cervical Cancer."

"Then you are a survivor."

"No!"

"Ma'am, help me to understand."

"Well I got sick, they did surgery and now they are wasting my time and want me to believe I need treatment. I am healed and all is well."

I really heard myself that day and it was disgusting. How can one be so sick and have so much pride? God must have thought, "This girl is a tough cookie. I have to strip her down further." Well, that is what he did. I got so sick from that treatment. I still had the tube coming out of my stomach to drain the cyst; I had to give myself a shot everyday to avoid a blood clot. It was so dark where I was. At times when I was so low, Andrea would call my friend and confidante, Pastor Dawn Harvey, and tell her to call me and pray. I would get calls from folks just in time and I always knew my friend Andrea was looking out for me. She was like a spy. She knew how much I tried to be strong so she would go to the appointments and pick me for information so she could stay on top of things. Pastor Dawn could relate to me because she had cancer as a young girl and it returned several times. She would pray and sow wisdom into me and cause a peace to set in. I am so grateful for her. My sister Bridgett went on my appointments as well. She would tell jokes because I looked so sad and would cry if I did not get my way.

There were days when, after I got to treatment, I would sit in the car in the parking lot and mentally shut down. I did not want to do it anymore. I would get a call from Mike asking me where was I. I am at the hospital.

Mike knew I played with words so he asked, "What are you doing?"

"I am sitting in the car because I do not have the mental strength to go inside."

"Okay then, I will stay on the phone with you until you get inside and I hear that receptionist say hello Ms. Jones."

Oh, I hated hearing her say that. She knew me because I had been there so many times. I did not want her to know my name anymore. Many days he talked me into the building and I am grateful for that.

At the six month mark the pain began to ease up somewhat. I could drive further and I could leave that bedroom that represented so much pain and warfare. I stayed at hotels to change the scenery and I would visit my friend Leslie's home where I got some relief. My niece Donnetta was so sweet. She would give up her bedroom so Aunt Lisa could rest and get better. I felt so much peace and relief when I would stay there that I visited quite often. I needed to get away.

I started to recover more and more. The energy would come and go but I learned how to handle that. I started working again and attending training sessions. The positive environment helped a lot. I had my good days and bad days but for the most part all was better.

MOVING FORWARD

The darkness started to be replaced with some light. I finally realized that God was not going to let me die. There were people praying for me worldwide. The sympathy cards were pouring in. My Primerica family sent fruit baskets at least three times a week. It was perfect because, for awhile, that was all I could eat. I received roses and floral arrangements. I received bracelets with positive quotes and scriptures. My friends, Sederick Thomas and Yvette Henderson, would call me to pray. The Jones Jewels leaders held the office together and kept the business running. I was blessed with monetary gifts. Before I could move forward with the surgery I was required to pay a large sum of money. If I did not come up with the money they were not going to perform the surgery. The thought of that was upsetting, but God blessed me through great leaders like Andy Young and Mike and Regina Evans. Their support went beyond the call of duty.

It is so amazing because so much of what I spoke from the stage and in training came back to me. I would always say, "Prayer is good but Prayer with a check is better." Well Andy, Mike and Regina blessed me spiritually and financially. My sister Bridgett Patten took off from work to be there for me day and night. She served me and cried with me. My niece who had gone through cancer and chemo at age fifteen, Briana Patten, was my advisor. If the doctor required something of me I would not do it unless Briana confirmed it. She helped me to make decisions because I was so sick I could not comprehend well. My daughter, Shanina Jones, never missed a beat. She stayed with me for over a month. She made it very clear to her employers that her priority was her mom. (tears) Last, but certainly not least, my parents, Walter and Angela Patten, prayed for me day and night. My mom would come into my room and hear me moaning in pain and she would lay hands on me and pray. It would immediately ease the pain and I would fall off to sleep.

Do you remember in the Physical Prosperity chapter where I talked about how I do the Daniel fast the beginning of every year? I was given two revelations during that fast last year, 2011.

In the first revelation God made it very clear that I was going to go to another level; and in the second, my mentor, Mike Evans, told me not to travel and speak as much that year because I had served quite a bit and it was my turn to be served. So I walked in that prophesy with expectation. I thought, "WOW a new level, awesome I am about to blow up in my business and my finances." I never imagined that the elevation would come in the form of cancer. I never thought when Mike said it was my year to be served that it meant I would be so sick that I had to rely on others. That absolutely blew my mind.

JOB experience ...

JOB 45:10-15

10 After Job had prayed for his friends, the LORD restored his fortunes and gave him twice as much as he had before.

11 All his brothers and sisters and everyone who had known him before came and ate with him in his house. They comforted and consoled him over all the trouble the LORD had brought on him, and each one gave him a piece of silver[a] and a gold ring.

12 The LORD blessed the latter part of Job's life more than the former part. He had fourteen thousand sheep, six thousand camels, a thousand yoke of oxen and a thousand donkeys.

13 And he also had seven sons and three daughters.

14 The first daughter he named Jemimah, the second Keziah and the third Keren-Happuch.

15 Nowhere in all the land were there found women as beautiful as Job's daughters, and their father granted them an inheritance along with their brothers.

I felt better so I started doing what I did best and that was praying for others and serving others. God placed in my heart to host a Women's Conference and title it, "I AM WISE, I AM WORTHY, I AM WOMAN" Conference. It was kicked off in November of 2011, and it was very successful. There is where I admitted for the first time some of my experiences and my mindset. I could see myself speaking again. I got my confidence back. I started seeing clients again and travelling again and training the agents again. There was some residue from the cancer and I still had rough days but the pain was not nearly as bad as it had been in the beginning. Treatment was over, I rang the bell of victory on the last day and promised the doctor that I would never return again to that department. She said I had better not. Thank you, Dr. Ottinger.

My JOB moment caused me to experience a lot in all five areas. I can tell you that I won the battle. The growth I had in the five areas kept me sane and even in my low times I managed to look up. I am forever grateful to God, my family and friends for all the love, prayers and gifts. I am a blessed woman and I have no regrets.

I am still pressing forward with all my might and I have accepted the fact that I am a Cancer Survivor. I am proud and I know now that cancer does not mean death. In my pain I grew more intimate with Christ. I love and trust him with all that I am. I am here today because of my Spiritual Prosperity. I started retraining myself Mentally through books, tapes and leadership events. My Physical Prosperity is getting better as a result of working out daily. I am blessed with Relationship Prosperity as you can see. There are too many to name but once again thank you Primerica family, African American Leadership Council of Primerica (AALC), Women In Primerica (WIP), The Jones Jewels organization, family and friends. You have blessed my life richly. My Financial Prosperity is being restored and God has made it very clear that I will not return to my comfortable place, but I will exceed far beyond my expectations. The LORD blessed the latter part of Job's life more than the former part. I receive that.

I CHOOSE LIFE AND LIFE MORE ABUNDANTLY

Chapter VII Journal Pages

Chapter VIII: Called To Action

Don't quit!

When things go wrong, as they sometimes will,
When the road you're trudging seems all uphill,
When the funds are low, and the debts are high,
And you want to smile, but you have to sigh,
When care is pressing you down a bit,
Rest if you must, but you mustn't quit.

Life is queer with its twists and turns,
As everyone of us sometimes learns,
And many a failure turns about,
When one might have won had he stuck it out.
Don't give up though the pace seems slow,
You might succeed with another blow.

Often the goal is nearer than it seems to a faint and
*   faltering man,*
Often the struggler has given up,

When he might have captured the victor's cup.
And he learned to late, when the night slipped down,
How close he was to the victor's crown.

Success is failure turned inside out,
The silver tint of the cloud of doubt,
And you can never tell how close you are,
It may be near when it seems afar.
So stick to the fight when you are hardest hit,
It's when things seem worst that you mustn't quit!

Author Unknown

Do you remember that I said I wanted to be an inspirational speaker? Inspired people take action immediately to get what they truly want. So it is time to make a decision. Do you want bigger and better? Do you want healthy relationships around you? Do you want a better lifestyle and financial independence? Do you want to be mentally stronger?

119

There is an old movie that I love and it is called *The Field of Dreams*. In that movie the main actor would hear a voice and the voice would advise him on what to do to make money for his farm. That inner voice wanted him to build a baseball diamond so that the players of old would come out and play ball and it said that people will come from all over. The inner voice kept reciting one phrase that was so profound to me. It said, "Build it and the people will come." My interpretation of that phrase was that he must change before the blessings would be bestowed upon him. Stuart Chase wrote, "For those who believe, no proof is necessary. For those who don't believe, no proof is possible." Well the actor had faith and he built the field even though the naysayers were taunting him and the bill collectors were harassing him.

So I say to you, fix you and the people will come. Fix your attitude, Self Esteem is given by self. Stop looking for someone else to give it to you. Change your mind. Speak life over your dreams and aspirations. Do not wait for someone to do that for you. Attach yourself to the right people; people of integrity and great character; people who are striving for bigger and better. Work on your physical and carry yourself like a professional successful individual. It is amazing how you will be received better.

Exercise makes you feel good inwardly and look great outwardly. Get a routine together. Do not compromise your health in order to achieve wealth then use up all the wealth in hope of getting your health back. You can build wealth or financial independence and stay healthy at the same time. Financially, make the necessary adjustments so that you are not worrying about how you are going to make it from day to day. It may require downsizing until things are in order. I know our economy went through a rough time but I really believe that people were still trying to keep the same entertainment budget even knowing that the cost of living has increased. Make wise decisions. Spending $300-$400 in groceries and still eating out three days a week is not wise.

I hope you enjoyed the Extreme MakeOver. Life is so wonderful and just existing is not acceptable. Make the necessary adjustments and put together an action plan that will allow you to prosper in all five areas. Thank you for allowing me to sow into you.

Chapter VIII Journal Pages

About the Author

Lisa M. Jones graduated from Baltimore City public school system and attended Johns Hopkins University. In 1994, she left corporate America as a graphics specialist to pursue her dreams of business ownership.

She is the owner of Jones Jewels and Associates, Inc. – a leadership training organization, as well as the owner of a financial services company. She is a member of numerous councils and serves as an Executive Board member of the African-American Leadership Council. Lisa has been the keynote speaker at over 150 Leadership schools nationwide since 1997. She has given thousands of speeches to diverse audiences ranging from 15 to 60,000 in attendance. In addition to keynote speaking, Lisa is a well-respected workshop trainer for many different government agencies including, but not limited to, GSA, EPA, FDA and VOA. Lisa has also personally coached, trained and developed hundreds of individuals seeking mentorship. She provides them with the fundamental leadership skills involved in building success.

Lisa draws on life experiences and over 17 years of business leadership experience to inspire individuals and organizations to maximize their potential and move from Vision to Reality.